The Geological Society of America
Memoir 77

RELATION OF ORE DEPOSITION TO DOMING IN THE NORTH AMERICAN CORDILLERA

BY

EDWARD WISSER

University of California, Berkeley, California

February 25, 1960

Made in the United States of America

TEXT PAGES COMPOSED AND PRINTED BY THE WILLIAM BYRD PRESS
BOUND BY RUSSELL-RUTTER COMPANY

PUBLISHED BY THE GEOLOGICAL SOCIETY OF AMERICA

ADDRESS ALL COMMUNICATIONS TO
THE GEOLOGICAL SOCIETY OF AMERICA
419 WEST 117 STREET, NEW YORK 27, N. Y.

The Memoir Series
of
The Geological Society of America
is made possible
through the bequest of
Richard Alexander Fullerton Penrose, Jr.

ACKNOWLEDGMENTS

The investigation described in this paper had its inception at The Johns Hopkins University, where the author held the Johnston Scholarship in geology, 1939-1941. Joseph T. Singewald Jr., then Chairman of the Department, actively encouraged the project, and Ernst Cloos gave generously of his wealth of structural knowledge. A liberal grant from the Penrose Bequest of The Geological Society of America in 1945, and another in 1947, were awarded for the express purpose of completing this monograph.

Thanks are due H. E. McKinstry for constructive criticism of the manuscript, and especially Ernst Cloos to whose thorough and illuminating labor of review the monograph owes its format and not a little of its content. My debt to the writings of Hans Cloos are apparent in nearly every chapter.

CONTENTS

ILLUSTRATIONS

PLATES

TABLES

ABSTRACT

Many structural domes and anticlines rise from undeformed surroundings; the general crust of the earth is neither shortened nor extended by these local swells or blisters, but the area of the plate upfolded is increased. With plastic material the increase is effected largely by flow; with brittle material, largely by fracture.

Many mining districts are associated with upfolds of this type. Districts here described fall into two categories: (1) those whose structural frame is a dome, and (2) those whose structural frame is an anticline.

Domes may show fractures which radiate from the apex, or concentric fractures which are segments of circles, of varying diameters but with a common center, the apex of the dome. Both types may appear on the same dome; the fractures of each type aid enlargement of the plate during doming.

Sunlight and Kirwin, Wyoming, are minor districts with dominant radial fracture patterns. Vein matter was deposited while the walls of the vein fractures were being pulled apart. With a radial vein system the only way in which all the vein walls could be simultaneously pulled apart is by stretching of the fabric of an expanding dome.

The structural setting of the Ophir, Utah, lead-silver district, and of the Matehuala, Mexico, copper district is that of a half dome truncated by a normal fault with downthrow away from the domical apex. Displacement on the fault is greatest opposite the apex and decreases progressively in both directions, becoming zero at the spring line. No part of the dome ever existed on the downthrown side of the fault, which was a fracture before doming. Maximum uplift was centered on one side of the fault and there produced the half dome; but the pre-existing fracture offered locally an easier mode of uplift by rise of the foot-wall block.

At Ophir ore shoots followed intersections on the half dome of radial fractures with limestone beds. At Matehuala stretching during doming was effected largely by flow of limestone, but a monzonite stock intruded in the half dome was too brittle to flow. The limestone pulled away from the unyielding stock; fractures concentrated around the periphery of the stock localized the Dolores copper ore bodies.

In the Silverton-Telluride district, Colorado, fractures radiate from a relatively large, roughly circular graben, along whose margin monzonitic stocks were intruded. Evidence suggests that this fracture pattern resulted from domical uplift, with the graben at the apex. Transfer of volcanic material from depth to the surface in the central area produced a sag which has eliminated the upward bulge of the dome.

Mineralization advanced outward from the graben step by step with the outward growth of the radial fractures. Copper–silver pipes within the fault zone bounding the graben were formed first, followed successively outward by base-metal deposits as veins, which were reopened to admit gold and silver, and by precious-metal vein deposits in the outermost zone.

The structural setting of La Plata, Colorado, is that of a dome, truncated, south of its apex, by a zone of high-angle faults striking eastward. Displacements on the faults are greatest opposite the domical apex. The doming is accentuated by a horseshoe-shaped hinge fold, open on the south. Along the fold dips of the strata steepen sharply; outside it, dips are gentle, whereas inside it, they are nearly flat. Several stocks were intruded along the fold, and others inside it. The steep flexural fold and abundant intrusions suggest upward shove of a flat-topped

1

piston, perhaps a magma column congealed in its upper part, but fluid and under pressure below.

Fractures are abundant along the horseshoe fold, and, with respect to the dome, fall into two classes, radial and concentric. Gold-silver deposits were concentrated chiefly within or near the horseshoe fold, and in the eastward-trending fault zone. Doming, which began during the intrusive epoch, persisted through the period of metallization, because at that time older fractures were reopened, new radial and concentric fractures were created, and fractures of both generations became loci for ore bodies.

The structure at Rico, Colorado, is that of a dome with eastern elongation. Superimposed upon the major dome, toward its eastern end, is a doubly plunging anticline, also with easterly trend, cut by fractures which parallel its axis, and by fractures normal to the axis. Rich ore bodies were localized at a stratigraphic horizon originally occupied by a bed of gypsum which was dissolved, leaving silty material which the ores replaced. Ribbon-shaped mantos lay directly above fractures, both of the longitudinal and transverse sets. Ore solutions ascended these fractures to form the mantos during late stages of the doming.

The Goldfield, Nevada, district lies on the southwest flank of a dome encircled by a belt of intense alteration, and of complex fracturing, which probably coalesces at depth into one or more persistent faults concentric with respect to the domical apex, and which formed the channel for altering and metallizing solutions. The volcanic rocks were brittle when first fractured by doming, but solutions rising along the fractures of the circular belt softened the rock by alunitization and kaolinization. Silica-bearing solutions then created the irregular silica "ledges" at horizons close to the then surface. The soft rock encasing the ledges flowed, as doming persisted, but the brittle ledges fractured. Ledges which had no "keel" below them were inaccessible to gold-bearing solutions; those with keels extending down to the main ore channel received the rich ore bodies.

Many mining districts are associated with doubly plunging anticlines, which with brittle rock are broken by fractures which strike parallel or normal to the axis.

At Creede, Colorado, older extrusive rocks were flexed into a north-trending anticline. Younger extrusive rocks do not share in the folding, but faults which strike parallel to the anticlinal axis and dip toward it cut and displace both older and younger rocks; they form a graben along the crest of the buried anticline. These faults originated as tension fissures, the result of arching of the older volcanic rocks. After extrusion of the younger volcanic rocks, renewed uplift was concentrated along the abutments of the arch, in the footwalls of the graben faults. These faults were propagated upward through the younger volcanic rocks.

The eastern graben fault, the Amethyst, fingers out at its southern end. Most of the silver ore of the district came from the southern segment of the Amethyst vein. Here intense local uplift in the footwall, unable to utilize the split-up fault as a lubricated plane of movement, tore apart the walls to permit entry of the silver-bearing solutions.

The structure at Bodie, California, is that of an irregular anticline upon which are superimposed several domes. The country rock is volcanic. Most of the faults and veins strike parallel to the anticlinal axis and dip toward it; but the Fortuna fracture, which carried the richest ore body, lies in anomolous relation to the anticline, for it is neither a longitudinal nor a cross fracture. It seems to have resulted from an earlier deformation, but to have been utilized by the uplift which formed the anticline in such a way that its flat segment gaped open to admit rich silver- and gold-bearing solutions.

Guanajuato, Mexico, lies on the northeast flank of a major anticline which plunges southeast. The anticline carries a crestal graben. The graben fault on the northeast flank is the Veta Madre, with maximum displacement on the northwest; displacement decreases progressively southeastward, in the direction of plunge of the anticline. Like the Amethyst fault at Creede, the Veta Madre originated as a tension fissure, but became an antithetic fault when the arch broke into segments under continued uplift. Major silver-ore bodies on the Veta Madre were localized where differential movement of the walls brought shallow cups in the footwall surface opposite planar areas in the hanging-wall surface.

At El Oro, Mexico, the attitudes of remnants of an andesite flow overlying shale, together with the fracture pattern, indicate deformation to form a broad anticline trending north–northwestward.

The San Rafael vein lies along a normal fault striking parallel to the anticlinal axis, with downthrow on the west, toward the axis. Faulting had been completed by the time of mineralization. Early, low-grade vein matter welded the fault, but arching continued and with it an urge toward resumption of faulting, prevented by the welding. The resulting strong shearing strain produced a number of vertical feather-joint branches in the hanging wall of the fault. These were mineralized by solutions rich in gold and silver.

The Mogollon, New Mexico, district lies on the west flank of a large anticline trending and plunging north–northeastward. The Pacific-Great Western and Queen faults strike parallel to the anticlinal axis and dip eastward toward the axial plane. The block between these faults contains a local bulge truncated on the east by the Queen fault. Displacement on the fault is greatest opposite the crest of the bulge and decreases progressively in either direction. The local uplift in the footwall increased the displacement on the Queen fault, but it took place in the hanging wall of the Pacific–Great Western fault. The original displacement was reversed in the segment affected by the bulge.

The bulge has the form of a doubly plunging anticline trending northward, parallel to the Queen and Pacific–Great Western faults. The chief productive veins of the district occupy cross fractures normal to the anticlinal axis. Most of those north of the highest point on the up-bowed axis dip southward, whereas most of those south of that point dip northward. These fractures gaped open, under continued bulging, in time to receive the richest surge of silver-gold solutions.

The following generalizations appear valid.

Uplift in these districts was accompanied by development of tension fissures. Uplift and consequent stretching of the arching plate persisted through the period of mineralization, but by this time stretching in many areas had reached a stage at which fissuring could no longer facilitate it; fissuring was succeeded by graben and antithetic faulting. Ore deposition sometimes preceded this faulting but more often followed it.

The fracture pattern on these domes and anticlines developed as uplift progressed. Solutions deposited vein matter in those fractures which were permeable at the time and accessible from the main solution channel.

Mesothermal deposits associated with domes and anticlines fall into groups defined by age of mineralization and by metallographic provinces, but epithermal deposits are scattered from one end of the Cordilleran region to the other. They show, however, a preference for major uplifts. Silverton, Rico, La Plata, and Creede lie on a tectonic element marked by recurrent uplift from the close of the Paleozoic to the Pleistocene. Epithermal deposits in Mexico are concentrated on the site of the persistently positive Occidental geanticline. The crystalline basement lies deep throughout much of Nevada, but Goldfield, Tonopah, and other epithermal districts lie above or close to relative highs in the basement which are much larger than the local uplifts with which these districts are associated.

These major uplifts were developing while epithermal metallization was taking place. The whole Cordilleran region was fast assuming its present shape. The local phenomena of uplift, fissuring, intrusion, and metallization were satellitic features superimposed on the uplift of the Cordilleran region as a whole. Because of this fact, a deep-seated origin for epithermal ores is suggested.

INTRODUCTION

A large proportion of petroleum production is from domes and anticlines of a certain type; for this reason oil geologists have studied them intensely, described them in detail, and suggested theories of origin. The author has seen many similar domes and anticlines during 30 years of field work in mining geology and has utilized data and ideas from petroleum geology to help interpret these structures. Scale-model experiments also offer suggestions concerning their origin. The writer has witnessed and performed such experiments and analyzed others described in the literature.

As a result, he is convinced that many domes and single anticlines result from differential vertical movement produced by forces directed vertically, at least in the upper portions of the crust.

The writer has applied the generic term "doming" to deformation of this type, whether the result be a dome or an anticline. Structures so formed grade from symmetrical domes through elongated domes to isolated anticlines which plunge each way and disappear and are not associated with corresponding synclines. Such structures have been called "blisters," "boils," and "tumors." They spring from relatively undeformed surroundings so that the general crust of the earth is neither contracted nor stretched by these deformations; but the area of the plate domed to form the blister is increased, and most of the increase is effected by fracture in brittle material and by thinning in plastic material.[1]

Domes and anticlines of the "blister" type are coextensive with fracture patterns which are repeated so consistently that there is no doubt concerning a genetic connection between the blister structure and its characteristic fracture pattern which developed as a result of stretching of the differentially uplifted plate.

Many mining districts in areas of layered rocks are associated with local "blisters" having the form of domes or of doubly plunging anticlines. The fact was pointed out long ago by Newhouse (1931) and others. For some of these districts sufficient data permit tectonic analysis by which is meant an attempt to determine the relations, both in space and time, between uplift, fracturing, intrusion, and metallization.

The districts analyzed are divided into two categories: (1) those whose major structure is that of a dome, and (2) those whose structural frame is that of an anticline. The origin of the type fracture pattern is discussed for each class and followed by description and analysis of mining districts which show that pattern. Its regional setting in the Cordilleran region is given for each district. Rock formations and structure are described next and are followed by an attempt to determine the mechanics of the structure. The mineralization and the relation of structure and tectonics to the localization of ore bodies are then described.

---

[1] No attempt is made here to define scientifically such terms as "brittle" and "plastic". In this paper a brittle rock is one that deforms, under given conditions, dominantly by fracture, although some plastic deformation may be involved, whereas a plastic rock is one that deforms, under given conditions, dominantly by plastic deformation or flow, although fracturing is usually also involved. By flow is meant simply change in shape without loss of cohesion of the body as a whole.

The 18 districts analyzed here and 89 others, also associated with blisters but not described, exhibit sufficient similarities to permit generalizations which clarify, it is hoped, the mechanics of fracture and "flow," and especially the control that structure and tectonics have exerted on the localization of ore bodies.

A structural map of the Cordilleran region of western United States and Mexico shows the distribution of these 107 "blister" ore districts in relation to major structural features, notably uplifts and depressions in the surface of the crystalline basement. Local blisters appear related to larger uplifts which are reflected in the basement, and the general relations clarify some phases of the development of the North American Cordillera as a whole.

Epithermal deposits which, in contrast to other types, show a distribution related to the structure of the whole Cordilleran region were formed only when that subcontinental uplift began to assume its present form. The opinion of Lindgren that epithermal veins were formed from solutions originating in reservoirs much deeper than the sources for other types of hypogene deposits is confirmed.

120°　　115°　　110°　　105°　　100°

BEARPAW MTS
LITTLE ROCKIES
25　67
26
IDAHO
BATHOLITH　QUARTZ HILL
BLUE WING
SUNLIGHT ⊗
KIRWIN ⊗
21
SALT CREEK FIELD
BIG MUDDY FIELD
45°
BIG HORN UPLIFT
BIG HORN BASIN
POWDER RIVER BASIN
CONTACT
JARBRIDGE
TUSCARORA
SEVEN TROUGHS
STAR PEAK　BULLION
LOST SOLDIER
OPHIR PARK CITY
SIERRA NEVADA BATHOLITH
BODIE 16
GOLDFIELD　ANTELOPE
24
DARWIN
40°
17
SILVERTON 18
RICO ⊗
LA PLATA ⊗　CREEDE
13　CALICO
MARBLE HILL
CERILLOS ⊗
35°
15
22
19
MOGOLLON
20
JOHNSON ⊗
27
29　5000
28
30
UPPER CRETACEOUS SEA
AXIS
32　33
SHORELINE OF
31　35
TERLINGUA
LAS DAMAS
LOS LAMENTOS　34
SANTA EULALIA
COAHUILA PLATE
COAHULA TROUGH
38
OCAMPO　36
39
37
40　PARRAL
41
MEXICAN
30°

TABLE 1.—*Sources of information for undescribed districts shown on Plate 1 (Continued)*

Number	Ore district	Reference
29	Sabinal, Chihuahua	Krieger (1935)
30	La Fortuna, Chihuahua	F. H. Lerchen and J. H. Parker (1929, unpublished report)
31	Las Cruces, Sonora	W. Taylor (1942, unpublished report)
32	Oposura, Sonora	R. N. Hunt and E. Wisser (1934, unpublished report)
33	Guaynopita, Chihuahua	Hovey (1906)
34	Boquillas, Coahuila	Anonymous (1917)
35	Aliados, Sonora	Wisser (1931, unpublished report)
36	Cusihuiriachic, Chih.	Donald (1935)
37	Naica, Chihuahua	Prescott (1926, p. 292–294)
38	Santa Elena, Coahuila	Fletcher (1929, p. 512)
39	La Mexicana, Sonora	Wisser (1936, unpublished report)
40	Batopilas, Chihuahua	Brodie (1909); Wisser (1944, unpublished report)
41	Los Ángeles, Chihuahua	W.A. Prichard (1909, unpublished report); A.W. Warwick (1906, unpublished report)
42	Minas Viejas, Nuevo Leon	Hayward and Triplett (1931, p. 13–15)
43	Potrero, Sinaloa	L. Price (1945, unpublished report)
44	Guanecevi, Durango	Terrones Benitez (1922); Terrones Langone (1940, unpublished thesis, Univ. Nac. Autónoma de Mexico)
45	Higueras, Coahuila	Hayward and Triplett (1931, p. 15–17)
46	Mitra Mt., Nuevo Leon	Hayward and Triplett (1931, p. 27–28)
47	Topia, Durango	W. Kane and E. Wisser (1946, unpublished report)
48	Velardeña, Durango	Spurr (1916, p. 610–611)
49	Cabacera, Durango	D. P. Wheeler (1948, unpublished report)
50	San José, Tamaulipas	Bastin (1937, p. 163–185)
51	San Nicolás, Tamaulipas	Bastin (1937, p. 187–197)
52	Cosalá, Sinaloa	Wisser (1947, unpublished field notes and compilations)
53	Guadalupe de los Reyes, Sin.	Wisser (1944, unpublished report)
54	San Dimas, Durango-Sinaloa	Wisser (1940, unpublished report)
55	Copala, Sinaloa	Santillán, 1929, p. 4–41); D. P. Wheeler (1948, unpublished report)
56	Sombrerete, Zacatecas	Wisser and C. B. E. Douglas (1928, unpublished report)
57	Candelaria, Zacatecas	Wisser (1950, unpublished report)
58	Sain Alto, Zacatecas	D. Gallagher (1944, personal communication)
59	Fresnillo, Zacatecas	Stone and McCarthy (1948)
60	Mier y Noriega, Nuevo Leon	Wisser (1944, unpublished report)
61	Canoas, Zacatecas	D. Gallagher (1944, personal communication)
62	Pinos, Zacatecas	Villafaña (1921)
63	San Pedro, San Luis Potosi	Lewis (1920, p. 444–446)
64	Comanja, Jalisco	Wisser (1944, unpublished report)
65	Angangueo, Michoacan	Lopez Nuñez (1928)
66	Los Azules, Guerrero	R. M. Hernon and Wisser (1946, unpublished report)
67	Judith Mts., Mont.	Weed and Pirsson (1898); Lincoln (1911)
68	Mazata, Jalisco	Barrera (1931, p. 53–60)

RADIAL AND CONCENTRIC FRACTURE PATTERNS
DEFINITIONS

RADIAL PATTERN: Fractures radiate from a common center like spokes of a wheel (Fig. 1D).

CONCENTRIC PATTERN: Fractures are segments of imperfect circles, for the most part, of various diameters but which have a common center (Fig. 1E). Where radial and concentric fractures occur together, the center of radiation coincides with that of the circles.

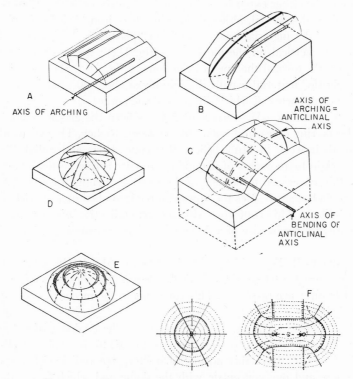

FIGURE 1.—*Tension fractures on anticlines and domes*

ORIGIN

Mechanics of doming.—No unique mode of origin can be assigned either to radial or concentric fractures, but the persistent association of radial and concentric fractures with isolated structural domes suggests a genetic connection.

An isolated structural dome rising from undisturbed surroundings may be the result of differential vertical movements produced by forces directed vertically. In this type of folding, called upfolding, there is no simultaneous contraction of the flanks, as in compressional folding. The crustal plate, which is domed, tends to be shortened normal to the surface of the dome and to be extended parallel to that surface because its area is increased by the upward bulging.

9

The extension or stretching of the plate may be resolved into two components, one of which acts concentrically with respect to the apex of the dome, and the other acts radially with respect to the apex. A circle inscribed around the apex before doming progressively enlarges as doming continues. The strain involved tends to be relieved by radial fracturing (Fig. 1D). The radial type of stretching is caused by an increase in the intensity of doming—*i.e.* by a rise in the dome in relation to its diameter. This radial strain can be relieved by concentric fracturing (Fig. 1E).

Field study and scale-model experiments show that radial and concentric fractures may be either extension ("tension") fissures or faults. Fissures develop where the domed material, although bending, acts in a "brittle" manner. Faults develop where the material tends to deform "plastically." Fissures, where they are radial, are vertical, in the ideal case (Fig. 1D); where they are concentric they dip inward, toward the apex of the dome (Fig. 1E). Radial and concentric faults in "plastic" material usually dip initially at about 60° and form a conjugate system, the components of which dip toward each other.

Magmatic doming.—Western Scotland has been the classic region for study of cone sheets, ring dikes, and radial dike systems. Richey, Thomas, *et al.* (1930), because of their work in Mull, believe that cone sheets and radial dike systems owe their origin to an excess of magmatic pressure acting vertically upward on a relatively thin cover and to doming of the roof of a magma reservoir. Where the magma cupola has steep sides the upward force is applied in a restricted area, and cone sheets form. This conforms with the generalization given above that concentric fissures form by rise of a dome without corresponding enlargement of its diameter.

According to Richey, Thomas, *et al.* (1930, p. 61-62, 93), where the magma reservoir has greater lateral than vertical extent and arches its roof gently, radial dike-filled fissures are produced. This conforms to the mechanics of radial fissuring offered above.

E. M. Anderson (1937, p. 36-37) shows that the tendency of a dome-shaped caldera to lift its roof forms tension fissures normal to the caldera walls, but that two sets of fissures have this normal character, one radial with respect to the domical apex, and one concentric with the dome and which forms the locus of cone sheets. According to Anderson, radial and concentric fractures may form together during magmatic doming.

Scale-model salt domes.—It is generally agreed that salt plugs forming domes in their cover rise vertically through the sedimentary rocks surrounding them, even though some of the uplift was relative, produced by subsidence of the surrounding beds. Parker and McDowell (1951) have produced striking scale-model imitations of Texas salt domes. In their experiments barite muds, representing sediments, overlay less dense asphalt representing salt beds; the only force causing doming was the density inversion. Part of the mud overburden was removed to initiate doming; after doming started the entire container was filled with the barite mud.

Radial fractures developed on every experimental dome. Transverse fractures developed also, slightly later than the radial fractures. In some cases the transverse fractures had strikes between those of radial and those of concentric fractures, but most of them were oriented as concentric fractures. An apical, roughly circular graben formed on most domes; in some cases grabens radiated from the apex.

The apical and radiating grabens formed as an integral part of the doming, and not during any later collapse. The graben floors subsided in relation to their frames, but both floors and frames rose with respect to sea level. The grabens dropped like loose keystone blocks where an arch is spread.

The experiments duplicate deformation in relatively incompetent rock, and the fractures produced are not fissures but faults which initially dip about 60°. Continued doming decreases the dip, in some cases nearly to zero. This flattening is caused by flow.

Clay experiments on doming.—Figure 2 is drawn from a photograph of a scale-model clay experiment performed under the writer's direction by H. C.

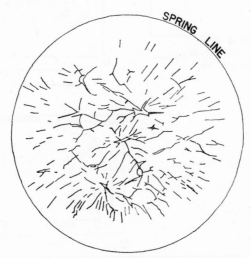

FIGURE 2.—*Experimental dome with radial fracture pattern*

Wells. A rubber pillow, circular in outline and overlain by a cake of wet clay, was gradually inflated. A dome formed in the clay cake, and fracturing developed on the dome. The dominant fracture system was radial, but concentric fractures formed also. Unyielding lumps in the clay produced local foci of radiation because they impeded uniform stretching of the domed cake.

The degree of doming capable of producing radial and concentric fractures is astoundingly small. H. Cloos (1939) produced radial and some concentric fractures at a stage of doming so slight as to fail to drain water from the apex of the dome (Fig. 3A).

It is well known that rocks in the engineering test laboratory and in the upper crust of the earth have extremely small tensional or stretching strength (Leith, 1923, p. 288; Nevin, 1949, p. 20). According to Leith (1923, p. 288-292) specimen rocks at the earth's surface fail under tensional pull at 1/20-1/40 of the stress under which they fail with compression, and at less than half of the stress that produces failure with shear.

Engineering test laboratory results do not apply to the depths of the earth where hydrostatic pressure exerts an enormous confining support which changes

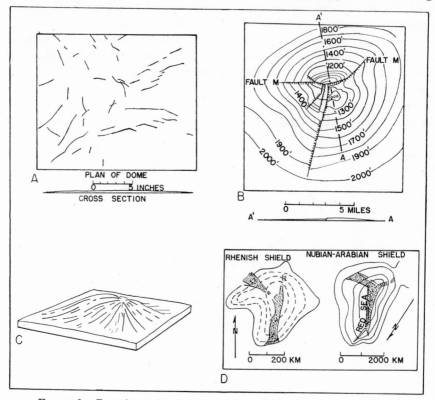

FIGURE 3.—*Experimental and natural domes with radial fracture patterns*

materially the behavior of rocks under deforming forces. But deformations considered in the present work took place at horizons not more than 1-2 miles below the former surface where the hydrostatic pressure was 1000 atmospheres or less. Rocks at such horizons may be assumed to be extremely weak under tension. It follows that even the gentlest doming tends to fracture the material being domed.

Homer oil field, Louisiana.—Cloos's experiment has a prototype in the Homer oil field (Spooner, 1929) illustrated by Figure 3B. Eocene sands and clays underlain by Cretaceous sands, clays, limestones, and sandstones are flexed into a dome 8 miles in diameter; the quaquaversal dips involved average less than 3°. The extreme gentleness of the dome is shown by Section A-A'.

The fracture system is radial, and the fractures are normal faults. One such fault, marked M on the plan, broke the upper portion of the dome into two segments, each of which had its own tectonic history during later phases of the deformation. Fault M seems to be composite and to consist of two radial fractures which meet at the domical apex. Spooner (p. 221) believes that tensional stresses induced by the initial upwarping broke the nascent dome along this fault. A genetic connection between the fault and the dome is suggested by the orientation of the fault on the dome and by the fact that the fault is limited to the higher portions of the dome. Displacement is at a maximum (500 feet) at the apex of the dome and decreases to the point where the fault disappears part way down the flanks.

After formation of the fault both the north and south segments of the dome continued to rise apically, but the south segment lagged behind the north. Whereas the fault is normal, displacement on it was effected by differential uplift. The north segment achieved its present form by doming, flexing of the beds in the area north of the fault, and by gliding of the edges of the beds differentially upward along the fault surface.

The south block continued to rise after the north block had reached its present form; this is shown by the fact that beds on the south side of the fault dip into the fault. Their normal dip down the south flank of the dome was reversed by an independent domical uplift with apex south of the fault. "The Homer dome is so obviously the result of vertically operating forces that further qualification of the statement is scarcely necessary." (Spooner, 1929, p. 219)

Major domes.—The Homer dome exhibits in its southwest quadrant a radial graben and a radial horst and resembles in this respect many of the Texas salt domes duplicated in experiment by Parker and McDowell. The Rhenish and Nubian-Arabian large-scale domes are depicted by H. Cloos (1939, Fig. 25) (Fig. 3D). Both domes show radial grabens. The Rhenish shield has two radiating anticlinal lobes, one of which has an axial graben which bifurcates where the lobe plunges toward the spring line of the major dome. The other graben lies on a normal flank of the major dome and is not associated with an anticlinal lobe. It resembles the graben on the Homer dome and those on the Texas salt domes simulated by Parker and McDowell.

The Nubian-Arabian shield is a stubby anticline or elongate dome. Its Red Sea axial graben bifurcates, like the tail of a fish, at each plunging nose.

Thus radial fractures on a dome resemble those on the plunging nose of an anticline.

MINING DISTRICTS WITH RADIAL AND CONCENTRIC FRACTURE PATTERNS

SUNLIGHT, WYOMING

REGIONAL SETTING (Pl. 1) : The Sunlight mining district lies in the northern Absaroka Mountains within the Yellowstone volcanic province. Elevations range from 7000 to nearly 12,000 feet.

Precambrian granite crops out not far east of the area (Parsons, 1939, p. 3), and the Precambrian of the Beartooth uplift is exposed within 25 miles of the district which is, therefore, a structural as well as a topographic high. The Tertiary pyroclastic rocks and flows rest on flat-lying Paleozoic (Middle Cambrian to Mississippian) sedimentary rocks. Since the total thickness of the Paleozoic rocks is only 2000 feet (Parsons, 1939, p. 2), it is evident that the Sunlight region was a platform during that epoch also. Presumably it was a structural high at the time of metallization.

ROCK FORMATIONS : Rocks of the Sunlight district are the extrusive and intrusive Tertiary volcanic rocks that make up the Absaroka range. Andesitic volcanic breccias interbedded with andesitic tuffs and flows are intruded by a composite diorite-syenite stock and by several basalt plugs which fed pyroclastic rocks and lava to a volcano 4-5 miles in diameter. The composite stock intruded one flank of the volcano (Fig. 4A).

Dikes, mainly of andesite, are extremely numerous. They fill vertical fissures radiating from the stock and arcuate fissures dipping toward the stock (cone sheets). A thick syenite-diorite ring dike lies south of the stock.

STRUCTURE : The fracture pattern is radial (Fig. 4A). Steep dike-filled fissures radiate from the composite stock through 360°. Concentric fissures (cone sheets) are discontinuous but with exceptions dip toward the stock.

According to Parsons, after formation of the radial and concentric fractures and their invasion by dikes, a second deformation caused renewed but less extensive fissuring which in part reopened older faults and dike-filled fissures and, in part, formed new fissures and "shear zones." The veins of the district lie entirely along fractures of this later period.

ANALYSIS OF STRUCTURE : The radial dikes and cone sheets strongly suggest doming by upward pressure of magma. Parsons states (1937, p. 838) : "An early period of fissuring and fracturing occurred during volcanic activity and intrusion. At that time, radial cracks were formed by upward and outward pressures due to volcanic explosions and the force of intrusion."

The Sunlight breccias, flows, and tuffs were extruded from the Sunlight volcano, the vent of which is represented by the basalt plug northwest of the stock. The extrusives dip away from this plug (Fig. 4B) so that their structure is depositional rather than tectonic in origin.

Doming sufficient to form radial and concentric fractures may be very slight (Fig. 3A). Where such slight doming is superimposed on an older quaquaversal structure, it would not ordinarily be detected.

15

Parsons states that much of the later fracturing at Sunlight took the form of "shear zones" which, from the context, appear to be sheeted zones. This use of the genetic term "shear zone" to denote a sheeted zone is unfortunate. Many

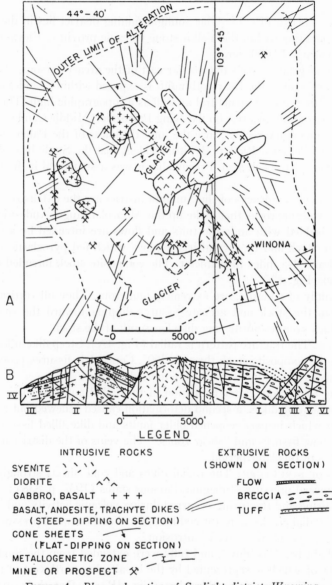

FIGURE 4.—*Plan and section of Sunlight district, Wyoming*

sheeted zones are manifestations of tension; the planes of sheeting lie normal to the direction of pull. Balk (1937, p. 27-33) points out that cross joints, which as a rule are longer and straighter than other joints, form in the upper consolidated portions of igneous masses whose still-fluid underlying magma is elongating in a direction perpendicular to the plane of the cross joints. Slight separation of opposite walls of the joints lengthens the solid rock body by rupture, whereas the underlying molten rock lengthens by flow. These are cross joints in the restricted sense. "In a broader sense, cross joints are identical with tension joints in the earth's crust." (Balk, 1937, p. 27)

Stretching of a crustal plate during doming would provide a mechanism for formation of tension joints as effective as that of the pull of underlying magma in solidifying plutons. The writer has observed systems of tension joints on domes and anticlines which consist of relatively narrow sheeted zones separated by areas less intensely jointed.

There is therefore reason for believing that the radial sheeted zones at Sunlight resulted from tension rather than from shear.

The initial fracturing at Sunlight which produced the radial and concentric dike-filled fissures is attributed by Parsons to magmatic doming, but he holds that the later fissuring that localized the veins was caused by settling and contraction of the extrusive and intrusive material of this volcanic center. Whereas many veins formed in reopened fissures and along dikes of the older system, some lie in fractures unrelated to that system. But gravitational adjustment, slumping, and other movements after the cessation of magmatic pressure would tend to push the walls of fissures together instead of pulling them apart. Therefore, it seems more likely that the late fracturing resulted from slight, continued or resumed domical uplift. This younger uplift was similar enough in position and direction to the older one to reopen many older fissures; but it differed enough to form fissures unrelated in attitude to the older sets.

METALLIZATION: The Sunlight district carries abundant, but narrow and discontinuous, quartz-carbonate veins of the base-metal type containing spotty silver and some gold. The main metallic minerals are pyrite, chalcopyrite, and galena, but proustite and wolframite are fairly common. The veins typically show crustified banding and drusy cavities. Many are of the "stringer" type composed of banded veinlets that mark a sheeted zone.

Parsons is not specific concerning the attitude of the veins although he states that some lie in "shear zones" along contacts with dikes, presumably of the radial system. His map suggests that most mines and prospects do lie along members of this system.

The mineralized area coincides with that of hypogene alteration (Fig. 4A). Within the limit shown most rocks are at least slightly altered by chloritization of mafic minerals and minor amounts of calcite, epidote, and pyrite. Areas of more intense alteration occur near the larger intrusive bodies and border the stronger veins. In such areas sericite appears in the feldspars, and chlorite spreads to the groundmass.

The district exhibits mineral zoning; metallogenetic zones are arranged in a layered domical structure, and the composite stock is at the core (Fig. 4B).

Zone   I.   Veins carry only drusy quartz and pyrite
Zone   II.   Chalcopyrite-pyrite-gold-quartz veins
Zone III.   Chalcopyrite-quartz-carbonate veins, mainly mineralized
                fault breccias
Zone IV.   Argentiferous galena-carbonate quartz veins
Zone   V.   Carbonate veins with galena, argentiferous tetrahedrite,
                and proustite
Zone VI.   Barren carbonates, minor quartz

Comparison of the mineral assemblage for the various zones with the para-genesis of the vein minerals suggests that mineralizing solutions moved outward and upward from the focal stock, and that deposits of the innermost zone, I, are the oldest, and those of VI, the outermost zone, the youngest.

RELATION OF STRUCTURE TO METALLIZATION : Proof that the Sunlight fracture pattern originated by doming is lacking, but indirect evidence offered above suggests it. The orientation and internal structure of the veins adds to the evidence. The veins are drusy and show crustified banding or occur as quartz-cemented rock breccias.

Berg (1932) shows that crustified banding and drusy cavities in a vein indicate that the vein-fissure walls were pulling apart while the vein-forming solutions were dropping their load within the fissure. A tabular body of brecciated rock occupies more space than it did before brecciation. Formation of such a breccia requires yielding of the rock on either side in a direction normal to the tabular zone.

Strikes of veins at Sunlight literally box the compass. The only way in which the vein fissures could be simultaneously pulled open is by stretching of the fabric of an expanding dome.

PRIMARY-ORE CHANNELS: Plainly the sheeted zones and reopened dike fissures which formed the loci for deposition of vein matter were merely secondary ore channels. These fractures are discontinuous, and the question arises, how did the mineralizing solutions gain access to them?

Mineralization took place after the intrusions had solidified, at least down to horizons within the zone of observation. The Sunlight stock cracked but little after solidification, shows little hydrothermal alteration, and is nearly unmineralized.

Nevertheless, vein minerals show distinct zoning around the barren stock. Higher-temperature minerals were deposited closest to the stock, and successively lower-temperature minerals farther away. Parsons infers from this spatial arrangement that the vein minerals are differentiation products of the magma that produced the stock. If so, unless the ore solutions originated within the exposed portions of the stock, they must have sprung from a hearth at depth. They could not have ascended through the tight, exposed portion of the stock, nor could the feeble sheeted zones in which the veins formed have acted as primary ore channels. The most likely trunk channel seems to be the periphery of the stock.

The attitude of the metallogenetic zones shown in section in Figure 4B suggests that the stock flares outward more radically at depth than the section through the stock indicates. This supposed flattening of the stock contact with depth seems especially plausible on the southeast side of the stock where the more important veins are found.

Mineralizing solutions moving upward along the gently sloping portion of the stock contact would have access to the steep tensional fractures over a broad area, and within the relatively shallow depth to which the fractures might be limited. Solutions rising along these steep fractures would have opportunity to encounter favorable structures within which to deposit their vein minerals because nearly the whole system of tension fractures lay within reach.

Toward the central, pluglike portion of the stock where the sides are steeper, the metallogenetic zones steepen also, as the section shows. Here intersections of the trunk channels, or sides of the stock, with steeply dipping fractures would be less numerous. Minerals of a given zone would find less opportunity to encounter favorable structures and form ore bodies. This might account for the fact that the better-grade deposits lie at some distance from the central stock and where the sides of the stock are flatter than elsewhere.

The close time relation between intrusion of the stock and metallization suggests a genetic connection, but the mechanics of ore-solution movement outlined does not preclude the possibility that the vein minerals zonally arranged about the stock have a purely structural relation to the latter and no genetic connection whatever. This has been discussed by Wisser (1941).

SOURCES FOR SUNLIGHT: Parsons (1937; 1939)

KIRWIN, WYOMING

REGIONAL SETTING, ROCK FORMATIONS, STRUCTURE, METALLIZATION: The Kirwin district, 60 miles south-southwest of Sunlight (Pl. 1) and near the south end of the Absaroka volcanic range, is mineralogically and structurally similar to Sunlight. Like Sunlight, it lay on a structural high when the veins were formed. A quartz monzonite stock intrudes andesite breccias and flows. Dacite and andesite dikes radiate from the stock; the ore deposits are mineralized sheeted zones which also radiate from the stock. "Structurally the deposits are essentially similar to those that have been termed 'lodes' in the Silverton district, Colorado, to which this district is in many ways similar." (Hewett, 1914, p. 126)

The gangue, of amethystine quartz, carbonates, and barite, is drusy. Metallic minerals are pyrite, chalcopyrite, sphalerite, galena, tetrahedrite, molybdenite, and stephanite. Crustified banding of ore minerals and gangue is common. Stephanite, the youngest mineral, lines drusy cavities in quartz.

Concentric fractures are not reported at Kirwin, but the deformation responsible for the radial fractures at Sunlight must have operated at Kirwin as well. Sheeted zones and the drusy, crustified structure of the Kirwin veins suggest that the deformation took the form of tectonic doming.

SOURCE FOR KIRWIN: D. F. Hewett (1914)

OPHIR, UTAH

REGIONAL SETTING: The Ophir district is in the Great Basin near the northwest edge of the Colorado Plateau (Pl. 1). Bingham is 10-15 miles northeast of Ophir.

At Sunlight and Kirwin the Precambrian basement was highly elevated and lay not far below these districts at the time of the mid-Tertiary metallization there. Conditions were quite different when the ores of Ophir and Bingham were deposited in early Tertiary time. The Paleozoic section is extremely thick here, although east of Bingham, toward the Plateau, the sediments thin abruptly.

In the Ophir-Bingham region the Paleozoic strata are folded into anticlines and synclines which trend northwestward in the vicinity of Ophir but regionally form an arcuate pattern convex to the northeast.

The Uinta uplift a few miles east of Park City (Pl. 1) has raised upper Precambrian sediments to elevations now exceeding 12,000 feet. The stocks and ore deposits of Park City and Cottonwood lie along the westward projection of the axis of this uplift. At Cottonwood a dome with Precambrian core intruded by quartz monzonite is broken by radial and concentric fractures. Here the Paleozoic section is relatively thin, but the belt of uplift, intrusion, and metallization continues westward into the region of thick sediments. At Bingham the belt is marked by a transverse arch superimposed on the Bingham syncline which plunges gently northwestward and southeastward away from the axis. The Bingham stocks and ore deposits lie along this linear transverse uplift.

This transverse belt is called by Eardley the Uinta axis (1939, p. 1282). The axis continues southwestward from Bingham and crosses the arcuate folds at right angles (Gilluly, 1932, p. 69). Each anticline and syncline plunges gently northwestward and southeastward away from this transverse axis of uplift. Where the axis crosses one of these folds, the Ophir anticline, uplift has been great enough to expose lower Cambrian rocks (Fig. 5A).

ROCK FORMATIONS: (In the immediate vicinity of Ophir)

Sedimentary Rocks

Age	*Formation*	*Symbol on Fig. 5 A*
Upper Mississippian	Great Blue Limestone	Cgb
	Humbug Formation; limestone, sandstone, quartzite	Ch
	Deseret Limestone	Cd
Lower Mississippian	Madison Limestone	Cm
Devonian	Jefferson (?) Dolomite	Not shown
Upper through lower Cambrian	Dolomite, limestone, shale, quartzite	∈

Total thickness of these formations is 8000 feet, but more than 15,000 feet of interbedded quartzite and limestone (Pennsylvanian) and 1100 feet of shale has been removed by erosion in the vicinity of Ophir.

Igneous rocks are limited to small rhyolitic and monzonitic stocks, dikes, and sills, for the most part strung along the northeast flank of the Ophir anticline.

STRUCTURE: The structure of the Ophir mining district is that of a half dome broken by radial fractures (Fig. 5A). The half dome lies at the intersection of the Ophir anticline with the Uinta axis, and the anticline plunges northwestward and southward away from the Uinta axis.

The half dome is bounded on the south by the Canyon and Lion Hill fault

zones which cross the anticline at right angles and dip steeply south. The faults
are normal step faults. The footwall of the Lion Hill fault is displaced strati-
graphically 1000 feet upward with respect to the hanging wall; the corresponding
displacement for the Canyon fault zone is more than 1500 feet.

ANALYSIS OF STRUCTURE: Butler (1920, p. 376) recognized a genetic relationship between the half dome and the Canyon fault: "The vertical force that
domed the strata apparently caused them to break along the line of the ("Can-

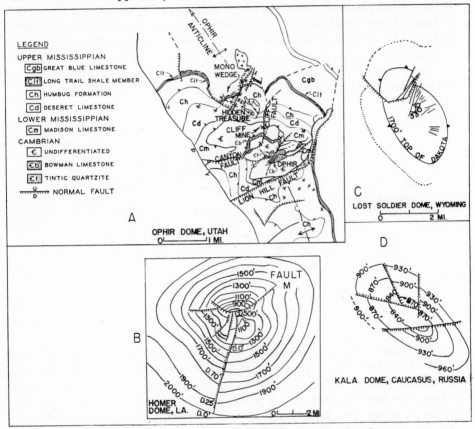

FIGURE 5.—*Ophir half dome, Utah, compared with other domes*

yon") fault and raised the portion to the north more than to the south . . . The
displacement was greatest at the apex of the dome and decreased both to the east
and west."

The dominant movement in this deformation was in a vertical direction, because the Canyon faults are steep. The fact that the faults disappear eastward
and westward toward the spring line of the half dome shows that doming and
faulting are parts of the same process, that of vertical uplift.

The fault system of the Homer dome (Figs. 3B, 5B) is not strictly similar to
that of the Ophir half dome, for on the Homer dome most radial fractures lie on

the downthrown instead of the upthrown side of the major fault, M. The mechanics of the later stages of doming at Homer, however, clarifies the doming at Ophir.

At Homer, Fault M originated at an early stage of doming; at this stage it had a half dome on its north side identical with that at Ophir. Displacement on Fault M is at a maximum at the apex of this half dome and decreases eastward and westward toward the spring line. After this faulting the block south of Fault M domed independently; its chopped-off beds slipped upward along the surface of Fault M and wiped out part of the earlier displacement. Thus doming forces on both sides of Fault M utilized this pre-existing break to facilitate apical uplift.

At Ophir the Canyon break was probably present as a fracture, with little or no displacement, before the doming. It is oriented as a cross joint formed by bending and stretching of the axis of the Ophir anticline (Fig. 1C).

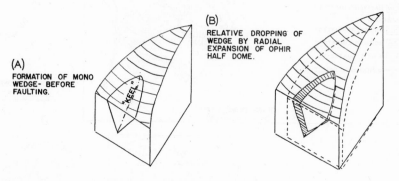

FIGURE 6.—*Mono wedge, Ophir*

The Mono wedge at Ophir (Figs. 5A, 6) is a minor but illuminating feature of the Ophir half dome. The wedge is formed by two radial fractures that join to make, in plan, a "V" open on the north. The wedge is shaped like the stern of a boat; the fractures join on dip to make a "keel" plunging northward. Beds within the wedge have been dropped 700 feet vertically with respect to those outside the wedge. Striations on the bounding fault are everywhere normal to the "keel" (Gilluly, 1932, p. 79).

Gilluly offers several mechanical explanations for the wedge but seems satisfied with none. The wedge is not difficult to account for on the assumption that the Ophir half dome swelled radially—*i.e.*, that it grew upward and outward from a focus of doming like an inflating balloon. A given area on the surface of a balloon expands, and, with expansion, points on the surface move radially away from the center of the sphere.

The Mono wedge was much like a loose brick in the domical roof of a furnace. Just as the furnace dome, expanding as a unit under heat, tends to move past the loose brick and cause a relative subsidence of the brick, so the Ophir dome, rising and expanding by flow, tends to leave the Mono wedge behind, even though the wedge block rises with respect to sea level.

Actually, the Mono "brick" was detached from its frame everywhere but on the north where it merges with the dome. Faulting around it was therefore of the trap-door variety.

The Mono wedge is a flaring graben on the flank of the Ophir half dome and resembles the radiating grabens on Texas salt domes duplicated by Parker and McDowell (1951, p. 7-8). In all these domes graben formation was a normal accompaniment of vertical differential uplift and had nothing to do with sag or collapse.

Gilluly (1932, p. 78) suggests that an intrusive plug underlies the Ophir area where the step faulting and doming may have been caused by upward shove of the plug.

Irwin (1926; 1929) describes the Lost Soldier dome in Wyoming (Fig. 5C) and shows that flow may accompany doming of the Ophir-Homer type. The Lost Soldier elongated dome carries radial fractures and a master fault which seems to have been formed by joining of two radial fractures with a central cross fracture normal to the axis of the stubby anticline (cf. Fig. 1C).

According to Irwin (1929, p. 649) the beds show marked stratigraphic thinning, caused by flow, on the northeast flank of the Lost Soldier dome. Similar thinning must have taken place in the beds of the Ophir half dome, if the mechanics advanced for formation of the Mono wedge is valid.

Figure 5D shows the Kala dome in the Caucasus (Goubkin, 1934). This elongated dome shows radial faults and a transverse fault somewhat suggestive of the Canyon fault at Ophir.

Evidence of doming is slight or lacking at Sunlight and Kirwin. Interpretation of the fracture patterns depends on analogy, experiments, and speculation. The striking half dome at Ophir, with its radial fractures and bounding fault, the displacement of which dies out in each direction away from the apex of the dome, clearly demonstrates the mechanics of doming and one mode of origin of radial fractures.

METALLIZATION: Lead-silver ore shoots tended to follow lines of intersection of radial fissures with favorable limestone beds; in such a bed ore extended either way from the fissure. In the Cliff fault ore zone, ore bodies were formed by replacement of blocks of dolomite or limestone within the confines of the fault zone.

At the Hidden Treasure and Chicago mines on the north flank of the half dome ore was deposited along radial fissures which fork with depth into branches diverging to the north. At the Hidden Treasure the shoots were pipelike with plunge to the north determined by the intersection of radial fissures with a particular horizon of the Madison Limestone. The Chicago shoots were veinlike, strictly following radial fissures.

RELATION OF STRUCTURE TO METALLIZATION: Gilluly (1932, p. 150) believes that time relations between intrusion, faulting, fissuring, and mineralization were close. The Canyon fault zone, the Cliff radial fault, and the radial fissures are all premineral. Both the Cliff fault zone and the faults bounding the Mono wedge carry tectonic breccia in places. Some of the ore in the half dome was deposited in open fissures. These facts suggest a tensional origin for the faults and fissures, and deposition of ore during the final stages of doming. After displacement on the Canyon fault, continued slight doming would provide the tensional pull on the walls of the fissures to keep them permeable to solutions. Butler (1920, p. 376) ascribes formation of the fissures to anticlinal bending of the limestone strata; but, if such bending had ceased before mineralization, the fissures would have closed by gravitative settling.

The trunk channel for Ophir ore solutions was probably the Canyon fault zone or the periphery of the buried transgressive igneous plug which supposedly intruded the fault zone, or perhaps both these features.

SOURCES FOR OPHIR: Butler *et al.* (1920); Gilluly (1932)

MATEHUALA, SAN LUIS POTOSI, MEXICO

REGIONAL SETTING: The Matehuala copper-silver-lead-zinc district is situated in central Mexico near the eastern margin of the Plateau (Pl. 1). It lies within the belt once occupied by the Mexican trough which reached its greatest development in the Early Cretaceous and started to break up in the Late Cretaceous.

The district is on the eastern flank of an irregular dome more than 20 miles in diameter which exposes upper Paleozoic sediments in its core. The silver district of Catorce occupies the crest of the dome which culminates in an anticline trending northwestward.

ROCK FORMATIONS: The sedimentary rocks of the district comprise a thick series of shale and shaly limestone underlain by massive Lower Cretaceous limestone. The massive limestone has been intruded by two monzonite stocks (Fig. 7).

STRUCTURE: The dominant structure of the western portion of the district is that of a half dome cut off on the east by a northward-trending normal fault (Fig. 7A). The fault throw is at a maximum at the apex of the half dome and decreases to zero to the north and south where the domical structure disappears (Fig. 7B, a section in the footwall immediate to the fault). This is not a faulted full dome because the block east of the fault where the writer has done field work shows no domical structure.

The monzonite intrusions occupy the central part of the half dome (Fig. 7). Although each intrusion contains one or more steep-sided plugs, they are in general complex assemblages of closely spaced dikes with sill-like offshoots.

A zone of intense fracturing hugs the periphery of the pluglike portion of the Dolores or southern intrusion. Some of the fractures lie just within the plug, but most are within the invaded rock. The fractures fall into two sets, one transverse to the contact, the other parallel with it.

ANALYSIS OF STRUCTURE: The overall structure at Matehuala is strikingly similar to that at Ophir. Both districts lie in geosynclinal regions where the stratigraphic section is thick. Both are local uplifts which lie on larger uplifts, although at Ophir the larger uplift is linear (Ophir anticline), whereas at Matehuala it is domical. Both structures are half domes cut off by normal faults. On each fault displacement is at a maximum opposite the domical apex and disappears either way, toward the spring line of the dome. The two districts seem to differ, however, in the fracture patterns developed during doming.

At Ophir, radial fractures were widely distributed over the half dome, whereas at Matehuala intense fracturing is localized around the periphery of the southern stock. At Ophir the rocks involved, mainly limestone, are homogeneous; no major igneous mass invades them, although one may lie deep beneath the half dome. At Matehuala two fair-sized intrusions break the homogeneity of the limestone; in doming the limestone could adjust itself by flow, but the igneous masses could not. The limestone apparently pulled away from the unyielding Dolores

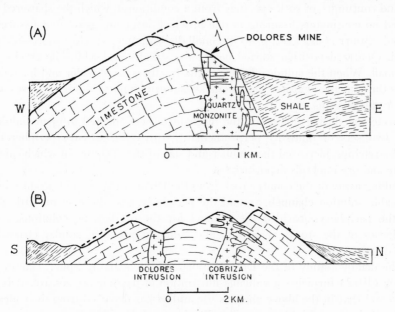

FIGURE 7.—*Sections through Matehuala half dome, Mexico*

plug during doming, and fracturing was therefore concentrated at the periphery of the plug.

These speculations gain strength from a study of ore deposition around the Dolores plug.

METALLIZATION: Copper ores were associated with both the northern intrusion and the southern or Dolores intrusion, but those of the Dolores area were the more important. The ores appear to bear a close genetic connection with the intrusion.

The Dolores intrusion was accompanied by intense contact metamorphism both without and within the igneous complex. The earlier lime silicates were deposited in irregularly crushed and shattered rock mainly along the periphery of the pluglike portion of the igneous complex. The distribution of the later lime silicates, hedenbergite and andradite garnet, however, was controlled by definite fissures, mainly along the southwest contact of the plug (Spurr *et al.,* 1912, p. 462).

Overlapping and subsequent to the deposition of andradite garnet, quartz, fluorite, chalcopyrite, and pyrite were deposited within the tactite bodies around the periphery of the plug. These ore minerals filled the fractures that are transverse to and parallel with the contact. Most of the veins are transverse to the contact.

RELATION OF STRUCTURE TO METALLIZATION: The entire cycle of deposition, from the earliest contact-metamorphic minerals through the ore minerals and ending with calcite deposition, was accompanied by a progressive increase in the size and continuity of rock openings from a condition in which the shattered rock showed no continuous fissuring to one in which large and persistent fissures developed (Spurr *et al.,* 1912, p. 465). Small discontinuous cracks progressively enlarged. Quartz deposition started before the sulfides and while the cracks were still small. When the sulfides deposited the fractures were wider and longer, and by the time calcite deposited, many cracks had grown to good-sized fissures which became calcite veins.

Stretching during doming is the mechanism best adapted to open simultaneously two sets of mutually perpendicular fissures. Progressive peripheral and radial stretching increased the number and size of the openings in which calcium-silicate and ore minerals deposited.

Pulling away of the country rock from the Dolores plug would produce highly permeable solution channels around the periphery, and there seems little doubt that the periphery provided the channel for the ore-bearing solutions, as the peripheries of the stocks at Kirwin and Sunlight provided similar channels in those districts.

The detailed study of the Dolores mine at Matehuala by Spurr, Garrey, and Fenner (1912) furnishes a valuable illustration of tectonic ore control. It is only fair to add that in the above analysis the author has departed from their ideas on the time relations of intrusion, mineralization, and doming.

SOURCES FOR MATEHUALA: Spurr (1916); Spurr, Garrey, and Fenner (1912)

SILVERTON, COLORADO

REGIONAL SETTING: The Silverton-Ouray-Telluride silver-gold-lead-zinc district is situated toward the western border of the San Juan volcanic plateau. The region is a topographic high with mountain peaks rising above 14,000 feet. It is a structural high as well: a relatively thin series of Paleozoic and Mesozoic sedimentary rocks rests on a highly elevated basement of Precambrian crystalline rocks and is overlain by a thick series of Tertiary volcanic rocks. In places the sedimentary rocks are missing, and the volcanic rocks rest directly on the crystalline basement. Precambrian rocks crop out at several places in the Silverton area (Fig. 8).

The San Juan region resembles therefore that of Sunlight and Kirwin where-relatively thin Paleozic sedimentary rocks lie on an elevated platform of Precambrian crystalline rocks and are overlain by thick Tertiary extrusive rocks.

Three major periods of deformation since Precambrian times are recorded in the San Juan region, marking respectively the closing phases of the Paleozoic, Mesozoic, and the Tertiary. Apical uplift was characteristic of each of these orogenies and was accompanied by production of monoclinal folds, tilted strata, and faults (Cross and Larsen, 1935, p. 110; Burbank, 1940, p. 197).

The great Paleozoic dome was peneplained before deposition of Mesozoic sediments. A broad uplift drove the sea from the region at the end of the Cretaceous or beginning of the Tertiary and was accentuated by a renewal of doming in the western San Juan province. The younger dome was coextensive in part with the earlier one, but extended farther west; its apex lay south of the Silverton quadrangle (Atwood and Mather, 1932, p. 15). Paleozoic and Mesozoic strata dip away from the apex.

Necks and dikes of granodiorite porphyry were intruded on the north flank of the dome near Ouray at a time probably coincident with this Laramide doming. Intrusion was followed by deposition of base- and precious-metal ores as blankets and veins in Paleozoic and Mesozoic rocks. The mining districts of Rico and La Plata occupy satellitic domes on the southwest flank of the major dome, and their ore deposits may date from this same period.

The major dome was peneplained, probably by Oligocene time, and the Telluride conglomerate was laid down on that erosion surface.

Recurrent major domical uplift marked, then, the pre-Tertiary history of the western San Juan region.

ROCK FORMATIONS: (Tertiary only)

Extrusive Rocks

Age	*Formation*	*Thickness*
		(Feet)
Miocene	Potosi volcanic series; rhyolite and quartz latite flows and tuffs	1500–3000
...	Erosion surface	
Miocene	Silverton volcanic series; andesite flows, tuffs, and breccias	1300–3100
...	Erosion surface	
Miocene?	San Juan tuff; andesitic and latitic tuff-conglomerate and breccia	100–3000

Sedimentary Rocks

...	Erosion surface	
Oligocene?	Telluride conglomerate	0–300

Quartz monzonite was intruded mainly as stocks; andesite and rhyolite were intruded as dikes, volcanic pipes, and irregular bodies.

STRUCTURE (Fig. 8): The structure is dominated by the nearly circular block of Silverton volcanic series shown in Figures 8 and 9. This block has been dropped 1000—2500 feet below its frame by a ring-fault zone. The faults are vertical or dip steeply inward. Intrusive masses, mainly quartz monzonite, are distributed around the ring; those on the south, especially, suggest by their shape that they were emplaced after or during the ring faulting.

Curved fractures outside the ring are concentric with it and dip inward at 60°–85°. Several carry dikes (Burbank, 1933, p. 177).

Innumerable fractures radiate from the central block. Figure 8 shows that

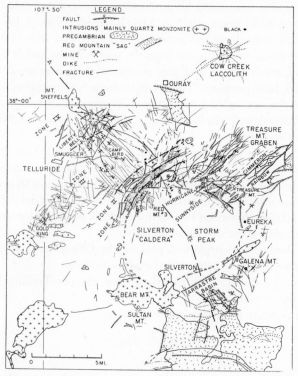

FIGURE 8.—*Structural map of Silverton district, Colorado*

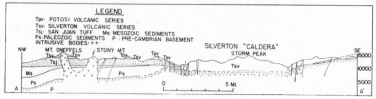

FIGURE 9.—*General section through Silverton district*

most of these lie in the northwest, northeast, and southeast quadrants; but they may be more evenly distributed, since the southwest quadrant has not been mapped in detail (Burbank, 1947, p. 421).

A number of radial fractures carry dikes, some of which are displaced by ring faults connected with relative sinking of the central block. On the other hand, concentric dike-filled fractures limit or deflect some radial fractures, and in the Arrastre Basin several faults acting along walls of radial dikes have offset concentric dikes with relatively large horizontal components (Burbank, 1933, p. 175, 178, 183-184).

Major faulting is almost limited to the ring faults bounding the central block. The block is slightly elongated northeastward. A zone of strong northeastward-trending faults lies outside the block but along the axis of its elongation. The faults enclose several grabens, the most important of which is that of Treasure Mountain, which in its southwestern portion has been dropped 1000 feet relative to its frame. The displacement decreases rapidly northeastward (Cross and Howe, 1905, p. 23).

The Red Mountain sag (Fig. 8) is a long and relatively narrow slumped trough in part coincident with a segment of the zone of ring faults on the northwest border of the central block, in part diverging from the ring to the northeast.

The Sneffels zone, a broader, milder downwarp, trends northwestward from the central block; its axis passes through the Camp Bird mine and Mt. Sneffels (Burbank, 1941, p. 217-227).

ANALYSIS OF STRUCTURE: Burbank (1933, p. 174-182) formerly thought that the concentric and radial fractures were developed by broad doming followed by dropping of the central block as peripheral intrusions, working upward, relieved the pressure that had caused the doming. Later (1947, p. 420) he abandoned this notion and ascribed the ring faults around the central block to caldera subsidence which commenced soon after extrusion of the Silverton volcanic rocks. The Silverton flows, tuffs, and breccias are thickest in and near the "caldera".

The concentric and radial fractures outside the central block are ascribed by Burbank to the action of large intrusive bodies which invaded the volcanic rocks and possibly domed them temporarily. As these intrusions cooled and subsidence centering in the "caldera" continued, further slight fissuring took place, and these late fissures admitted ore-bearing solutions (Burbank, 1947, p. 420). This resembles Parson's mechanics for Sunlight and is open to the same objections.

In the writer's opinion the Silverton fracture pattern, including the central dropped block, owes its origin to broad doming, because:

(1) Domical uplift deformed the western San Juan region twice before and once after the Silverton radial and concentric fracture pattern was produced. Ernst and Hans Cloos (1934) point out that the Beartooth, Big Horn, and Black Hills Tertiary uplifts are rejuvenated domical structures dating from the Precambrian. Uplift in the San Juan region recurred more persistently. In the central part of the district, the San Juan tuff thins rapidly southeastward and northwestward, toward the central block or "caldera" and pinches out near the borders of the block, within which the Silverton volcanic rocks rest directly on the Precambrian (Fig. 9). A bedded formation like the San Juan tuff may thin from several causes: diminution of material away from its source, in this case volcanic vents (this is plainly not the case here); deposition around a mountain mass which remained as an island rising above the tuff series; domical rise of a portion of the basement during or after deposition of the tuff and stripping by erosion of any tuff deposited in the area domed.

A mountain mass around which the tuff deposited could have formed only by apical uplift of the Telluride erosion surface, in which case maximum doming occurred just before extrusion of the San Juan tuff, because it is unlikely that any "bumps" of the older "Laramide" dome, whose apex lay south of the Silverton quadrangle, could have persisted into the Miocene.

Where the Silverton volcanic series overlies San Juan tuff, it fills great canyons carved through the tuff series and extending in places below the level of the Telluride erosion surface upon which the San Juan tuff was deposited (Atwood and Mather, 1932, p. 18).

Formation of such gorges is commonly attributed to uplift proceeding concurrently with downcutting of streams (Grand Canyon). The alternative possibility therefore seems the most likely: domical uplift was initiated during deposition of the San Juan tuff and persisted through the epoch of deposition of the Silverton volcanic series which was poured forth upon a dome from vents produced by the doming.

After extrusion of the Silverton volcanic series, continued vigorous erosion carved out another set of mighty gorges in those rocks; the gorges were filled by the succeeding Potosi volcanic series.

The case for persistent uplift is strengthened by the fact that probably no coarse detrital material produced by the cutting of such gorges remains in the district. The material must have been removed by consequent streams with steep gradients, radiating from the domical uplift.

(2) The Silverton fracture pattern is one typically associated with domical uplifts. Radial fractures on domes are almost universal. Apical grabens, represented at Silverton by the central block, are often developed during doming.

(3) A radial fracture pattern produced by doming is in full view northeast of Ouray (Fig. 8). The Cow Creek latite intrusion is a partial laccolith according to Cross and Howe (1907, p. 11). It intruded conformably with the beds of the San Juan tuff everywhere but on the south where it cut across the beds. Dikes radiate from the intrusion everywhere but on the south, the only side where doming of the strata did not take place.

(4) Figure 10 illustrates an experiment by Ekkernkamp (1939, Fig. 26). A wetted clay cake was molded above a deflated circular pillow. A hard cylindrical lump was inserted in the clay above the center of the pillow. The pillow was inflated with its lower surface held firmly to the table, thus doming the clay above it.

Radial fractures developed step by step with the doming. The clay above the hard lump rose as an apical horst surrounded by a zone of ring faults. The experiment was designed to imitate a graben ring surrounding a Precambrian pluton in Sweden.

The clay cake was still doming when the grabens developed. The graben blocks rose in relation to the table, but lagged behind the rest of the dome like the Mono wedge at Ophir.

In doming, the clay stretched and fractured everywhere except above the central lump. The flanks of the dome pulled away from the unyielding lump and formed tension fractures around it similar to those formed around the Dolores plug at Matehuala. The clay over the central lump did not fracture because all strain there was relieved by the peripheral fracturing. The Dolores plug also is only slightly fractured.

Whereas the fracture pattern at Silverton resembles that of the experiment, the central block in the experimental dome is elevated above the rest of the dome, and that at Silverton is depressed. The central lump in the experiment acted like a piston transmitting to the surface the uplifting force of the inflating pillow. Had there been no lump an apical graben like the central block at Silverton would have developed. There was no resistant lump or upward-shoving piston beneath this block; on the contrary, there may have been a semivoid caused by transfer of the mass of Silverton volcanic rocks from depth to the surface.

Since strain in the central block was relieved by ring faulting around it, little fracturing took place within the block.

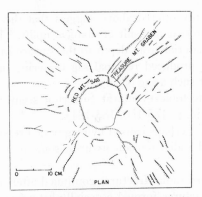

FIGURE 10.—*Experimental dome with hard kernel at apex*

At Silverton, as in the experiment, the radial fracture system includes grabens, and minor grabens border the central block at Silverton in a manner suggestive of the graben ring on the experimental dome.

(5) Ring faults bounding the central block in the Red Mountain segment show no evidence of strong shearing strain along them; some members of the system are merely shatter zones. This fact and the nature of the fracture pattern suggest (Moehlman, 1936, p. 385) that the ring faults were formed in response to tension during doming.

A fault may form as a result of shearing strain, or it may originate as a tension fissure and be transformed into a fault by gravity. After movement begins on either type, pressure normal to its walls plus friction may oppose the movement and set up shearing strain in the adjacent wall rock. Although some shearing strain occurs wherever two fault blocks move past each other, the strain may be severe or negligible, depending on the attitude of the fault and the nature of the deformation.

The central block at Silverton may be a caldera, as Burbank supposes, formed by subsidence into a semivoid that was produced by transfer of the Silverton volcanic series from below to the surface. If this be the case, the ring faults should show evidence of strong shearing strain because material surrounding the semivoid tends to crowd centripetally into it. The ring faults apparently fail to show such strain. The dropping of an apical graben during doming, although brought about by gravity, is triggered by the pulling away from it of the rising and expanding material around it (Mono wedge and Ophir). The graben faults should show a minimum of shearing strain.

The stocks along the zone of ring faults suggest by their shape, and by their blotting out of the faults in places, that they intruded during or after the faulting (Fig. 8). Plutons seem to make their way into areas of low pressure or tension.

(6) Concentric fractures outside the central block dip 60°-80° inward. Many of these are cone sheets; the production of cone sheets by upward magmatic pressure has been discussed.

The lines of evidence offered above suggest that the Silverton central block dropped below its frame as a result of domical uplift. This does not imply that transfer of volcanic material from depth to the surface in the area of the central block might not have produced regional sag centering in the area of the block. Figure 9 suggests that such a sag occurred.

The sequence of tectonic events at Silverton seems to have been about as follows (Burbank, 1933, p. 175-176, 183-184).

(1) Early doming, perhaps caused by magmatic pressure, followed by formation of concentric and radial tension fissures, some of which were immediately filled with dikes.

(2) Development of radial fractures continued after most concentric fissures had formed. Radial fractures formed especially between older concentric breaks.

(3) Peripheral faulting around the central block now reached its culmination, while radial fractures continued to form. Stocks invaded the ring-fault zone around the central block.

(4) Doming continued, although diminished in force. The central block dropped no farther because its bounding faults were for the most part sealed by intrusion.

(5) Upward pressure which caused the doming gradually diminished. As it diminished the heavy load of Silverton volcanic rocks concentrated in the central area tended by its weight to counteract the upward pressure and, as the pressure still further lessened, to subdue it entirely. The general sag of the central area shown in Figure 9 was the final result. Since the ring faults around the central block were by now sealed by intrusion, the plug could no longer drop, and the sag extended beyond it out into its frame.

METALLIZATION: The complexly fractured Silverton region is the structural setting for ore deposits which have yielded more than a third of a billion dollars in gold, silver, lead, zinc, and copper.

Metallogenetic zoning is closely related to structure. Burbank (1940, p. 246-

248) recognizes four such zones in the Red Mountain-Telluride-Mt. Sneffels area. The zones are shown in Figure 8 and described in Table 2.

Comparable zoning occurs south and southeast of the central block (Burbank, 1933, p. 165-166). Ore bodies in the southeastward-striking radial fissures near the central block carried abundant galena with sphalerite and chalcopyrite in a quartz and chlorite gangue. A mile to the southeast the same fissures carry fewer base metals, argentiferous tetrahedrite becomes important, and barite and rhodochrosite appear. Still farther southeastward the same fissures carry only barren quartz and calcite.

Crustified banding and drusy cavities are common in the veins, although some veins are not banded. A number of veins, for example the Camp Bird, are mineralized sheeted zones. Within the individual fissures of such a zone the vein matter has crystallized in open spaces. Many veins show intramineral brecciation; earlier vein matter was broken into angular fragments by renewed movement along the fracture and recemented by fresh vein matter (Ransome, 1901b, p. 87-92).

The Silverton veins resemble closely those of Sunlight and Kirwin.

RELATION OF STRUCTURE TO METALLIZATION: Control of ore deposition at Silverton was almost exclusively tectonic.

"The local control of ore deposition and distribution of ore shoots . . . in any mineral zone appears related primarily to the timing of local fissure opening with respect to the successive stages of mineralization. Parts of a fissure zone opened only during the base-metal stage contain little gold and, except in the outer parts of the intermediate zone," (III)" little silver; however, because of the widespread influence of the stronger stages of fissuring, many of the more persistent veins of the intermediate zone contain minerals of all stages at one position or another. Where repetitions of movements of like kinds have occurred the deposits of the different stages are likely to be coextensive . . . In some sectors where the growth of fissure zones appears to have advanced outward from the structural center with successive stages of fissuring, the part of a zone that is farthest from the center may contain a relatively greater bulk of late stage minerals." (Burbank, 1940, p. 252)

Mineralization at Silverton took place in four main stages and several substages (Burbank, 1940, p. 248-252). Table 2 summarizes the characteristics of the various stages and shows where their minerals were deposited in the northwest part of the district.

The earliest minerals, those of Stages 1A and 1B, were deposited only in Zones I and II, within a mile of the central block. During Stage 2A mineralization still tended to hug the central block, for the base-metal ores of that stage were deposited mainly in Zone II.

Mineralizing solutions spread farther from the central block during Stage 2B and penetrated all of Zone III. Sulfides decreased in relative bulk and changed in type from zinc to lead-silver ores. In Stage 3 sulfides decreased still further. The massive pyritic bodies of Stage 1B were ripped open in Zone II, and gold of Stage 3A was deposited in the openings; ore was thus made out of previously barren material. New veins carrying silver and gold with minor sulfides were formed in Zone II and parts of Zone III.

Stage 3B was characterized by reopening of veins, largely those of Zone III, by growth of these vein fissures outward into Zone IV, and by formation of new

TABLE 2.—*Metallogenetic zones in northwest portion of Silverton district*

Zone	Position	Structure	Mineralization	Stage of deposition
I	In ring-fault zone (Red Mt. sag)	Complexly faulted sag trough. Shallow-seated intrusives	Copper-silver pipe deposits with pyrite and galena. Associated spatially with the intrusives	1A
			Massive pyrite vein deposits	1B
II	"Inner" zone, next to Zone I. Maximum width 1 mile	Network of discontinuous fractures belonging to radial, concentric and anomolous systems	Complex Zn-Pb-Cu ores, quartz gangue. Low Au, Ag	2A
			Reopening of some fissures permitted entry of late gold	3A
			Reopening	
			Deposition of barren quartz and fluorite	4
III	"Intermediate" zone, extending 3–5 miles outside of Zone II	Radial fractures dominate and carry the ore	Complex base-metal ores, low Au, Ag	2A
			Reopening	
			Lead-silver ores, argentiferous galena and tetrahedrite in quartz-barite gangue	2B
			Reopening	
			Gold-silver ores with minor chalcopyrite, sphalerite, galena, quartz gangue	3A
			Reopening	
			Deposition of high-grade gold-quartz ores	3B
			Reopening	
			Deposition of barren quartz and fluorite	4
IV	"Outer" zone	Only strongest radial fractures of inner zones persist. They carry the ore	Silver-gold ores in quartz-carbonate gangue. No base-metal ores	3B
			Reopening	
			Deposition of barren quartz	

vein fissures in Zones III and IV. Veins of this stage carried high gold content, with tetrahedrite and ruby silver.

During Stage 4 barren quartz was deposited throughout the various mineral zones and indicated a general reopening of fissures.

This description applies to the northeast quadrant of the radial fracture system. The Sunnyside vein lies in the northwest quadrant and fills a radial fissure striking northeastward (Fig. 8). The ore bodies lay close to the intersection of the Sunnyside vein and a ring fault which bounds the central block. Hulin (1929, and Personal communication) recognized four stages of mineralization.

TABLE 3.—*Stages of mineral deposition at Sunnyside*

Stage	Minerals	Equivalent stages, northwest part of district
1	Massive pyrite and quartz	1B
	Reopening	
2A	Massive galena, blende, some chalcopyrite, quartz gangue	2A
2B	Argentiferous tetrahedrite	2B, in part
	Reopening	
3	Rhodonite, with some silver sulfide at start; quartz	2B, in part (vein minerals include rhodochrosite)
	Reopening	
4	High-grade gold-quartz	3A, 3B

Sunnyside lies in what would correspond to Zone II of the northwest area. The mine produced lead and zinc with relatively low silver content; this was the principal ore type also for Zone II.

Thus mineralization at Silverton followed step by step the formation of the fractures in which the vein matter was deposited. Higher-temperature minerals were deposited nearest the ring-fault zone, which seems to have been the trunk channel for ore solutions. In general, successively lower-temperature minerals were deposited farther and farther outside the central ring. But while relatively low-temperature precious-metal ores were deposited mainly in Zone III, 4-6 miles outside the central ring, similar ore bodies formed near the ring by reopening high-temperature massive pyrite veins there.

As mineralization proceeded the solutions progressively changed in composition and dropped in temperature even within their trunk channel. They made their way outward along radial fissures that grew centrifugally from the structural center under a persistent or recurrent stress that also reopened older, inward segments of the radial fissures. As the master fissures grew radially outward, solutions successively lower in temperature and changing from base-metal to precious-metal types filled them with vein matter to produce metallogenetic zones concentric with the central ring.

The solutions that deposited the younger vein matter in newly formed fractures far outside the central ring were not forced to pass through reopened older veins near the ring. As fracturing spread from the center outward, the fractures tapped deeper and deeper crustal layers because the depth of a fracture may be assumed to increase directly with its length. Few radial fractures connected directly with the trunk channel, presumably the ring-fault zone; but the complex, intensely developed fracture pattern must have offered continuous, if devious, solution channels.

Ore solutions could therefore leave their trunk channel at deeper and deeper horizons as the fractures radiating from it grew in length. These younger solutions could pass under the older, higher-temperature vein matter that filled segments of fractures nearer the central block, and drop their load far from the trunk channel, in newly made extensions of older radial fissures, or in independent fissures just coming into being.

The mechanics of vein formation at Silverton accords well with ideas of the origin and growth of the fracture pattern derived from purely tectonic considerations.

SOURCES FOR SILVERTON: Atwood and Mather (1932); Burbank (1933; 1940; 1941); Cross and Howe (1905; 1907); Cross and Larsen (1935); Kelley (1946); Moehlman (1936); Ransome (1901b)

LA PLATA, COLORADO

REGIONAL SETTING: La Plata mining district occupies a satellitic dome on the southwest flank of the major dome with apex south of Silverton, which formed at the end of Cretaceous or beginning of Tertiary time (Pl.1). The regional dip of the Paleozoic and Mesozoic strata locally domed at La Plata is to the southwest.

ROCK FORMATIONS:

Sedimentary Rocks

Age	Formation	Thickness (Feet)
Upper Cretaceous	Mancos shale	1200 (Only lower part exposed)
	Dakota sandstone	100–150
Upper Jurassic	Morrison formation; sandstone and shale	400–625
	Junction Creek sandstone	160–500
	Wanakah formation; marl, sandstone, limestone	0–150
	Entrada sandstone	100–265
Jurassic? and Upper Triassic	Dolores formation; "red beds"	500–750
Permian	Cutler formation; "red beds"	1500–2200
	Rico formation; shale, sands one	100–300
Pennsylvanian	Hermosa formation; sandstone, shale, limestone	500 (exposed)

Intrusive rocks
(In order of relative age)

(1) Porphyritic rocks, from diorite to monzonite, as stocks, dikes, and sills
(2) Nonporphyritic monzonite stocks
(3) Nonporphyritic syenite stocks
(4) Nonporphyritic diorite stocks

STRUCTURE: The La Plata dome (Fig. 11) is 15 miles in diameter and has a vertical rise of 6000 feet and a ratio of vertical rise to diameter of 1:14. Nearly

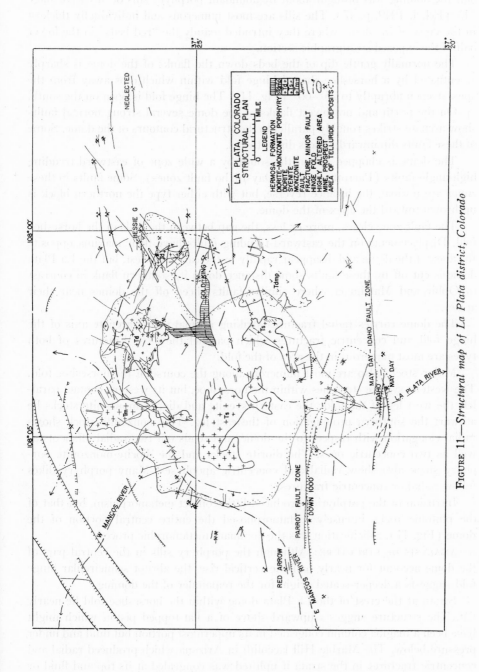

FIGURE 11.—Structural map of La Plata district, Colorado

half the doming was brought about by abundant porphyry sills of intrusive stage (1) (Eckel, 1949, p. 47). The sills are most numerous and individually thickest in the crest of the dome where they intruded mainly the "red beds" in the lower half of the exposed stratigraphic section.

The normally gentle dip of the beds down the flanks of the dome is sharply accentuated by a horseshoe-shaped hinge fold within which dips away from the apex steepen abruptly to 25°–60° (Fig. 11). The hinge fold is open on the south.

On the north and northwest flanks of the dome several strong normal faults show arcuate strikes roughly parallel to the structural contours of the dome. Some of these faults dip inward, others dip outward.

The dome is chopped off on the south by a wide zone of eastward-trending high-angle faults (Parrott and May Day-Idaho fault zones). Some faults in these zones are normal, the balance reverse, but with either type the northern block is upthrown toward the apex of the dome.

The fault zone closes, more or less, the gap between the ends of the horseshoe fold. Displacements on the eastward-trending faults have their maxima opposite the apex of the dome and disappear rapidly to the east and west, but the La Plata dome is cut off by these faults some distance down its southern flank in contrast to Ophir and Matehuala where similar faults sliced off the domes near their apices.

The dome carries radial fractures striking normal to the arcuate axis of the hinge fold and concentric fractures which parallel the axis. Fractures of both types are most numerous in the area of the fold.

Major stocks also are most numerous along the course of the horseshoe fold. The western syenite stock lies within the horseshoe, but its western contact parallels the west leg of the fold; the eastern syenite and diorite-monzonite stocks lie athwart the southern prolongation of the east leg. The monzonite stock shows radial elongation with respect to the dome, and sends out two radial offshoots as well as two concentric ones. The diorite stocks and the diorite-monzonite porphyry stock also show radial and concentric apophyses. Many porphyry dikes follow radial or concentric fractures.

Intrusion of the porphyries produced little contact metamorphism, but that of the plutonic rocks intensely metamorphosed the entire central portion of the dome (Fig. 11). Silicification was the dominant metamorphic process.

ANALYSIS OF STRUCTURE: Although the porphyry sills in the central part of the dome account for nearly half the vertical rise, the abrupt semicircular hinge fold suggests a deeper-seated origin for the remainder of the doming.

Strata at the crest of the La Plata dome within the horseshoe fold lie nearly flat. The structure suggests upward shove of a flat-topped piston which might have been a magma column congealed in its uppermost portion but fluid and under pressure below. The Marble Hill laccolith in Arizona which produced radial and concentric fractures in the strata it uplifted was congealed at its top and fluid or viscous below at the time it intruded, according to Robinson (1913, p. 70-74, Figs. 16, 17). If the magma at La Plata occupied a vertical cylindrical conduit, magmatic pressure at depth would force the solid top upward like a piston. The steep periphery of the piston moving upward through the punctured rock would act as a cutting tool and would generate a peripheral fault shaped like a well casing. Such a fault would work upward ahead of the rising piston, and on leaving the brittle crystalline basement to enter the bedded and flexible cover the fault would change to a flexure, the hinge fold at La Plata. Thom (1923) has shown that high-angle faults in the basement may pass into hinge folds in the cover.

Continued upthrust of the piston would tend to break the ring fold by radial stretching and to open concentric fissures along the fold axis. But the strata would be domed by the centrically directed uplift; the dome as it rose would stretch concentrically as well as radially, and concentric stretching would open radial fractures.

The rising and expanding dome would pull away from the central block bounded by the ring fold in the cover and the ring-fault zone in the basement, just as a dome at Silverton would pull away from a central graben. The ring faults would tend to open in each case; if they tapped still-fluid magma at depth the magma would rise along the permeable faults to form the ring of stocks that marks each district.

Doming was probably operating at La Plata throughout the periods of porphyritic and plutonic intrusion, because stocks of both types send out radial and concentric apophyses, and most dikes follow fractures of these systems.

The La Plata deformation is imitated by two experiments. Tension around the rising plug of the Ekkernkamp clay experiment (Fig. 10) is shown by the ring graben around the plug. If magma had been available it might well have invaded this ring-fault zone.

An experiment designed to imitate La Plata was performed by H. C. Wells (Fig. 12). A cylindrical flat-topped plug was thrust up into a clay cake. A circular hinge fold formed above the periphery of the plug. The central area above the plug remained nearly flat and almost unfractured, but concentric fractures in the hinge-fold zone were opened by continued rise of the plug. The rising plug created a gentle dome outside the circular flexure. The dome expanded peripherally and produced radial fractures.

METALLIZATION: Ore deposits are few in the flattish apical part of the dome inside the horseshoe fold. Gold-silver-telluride ores furnished most of the production. Ores of this type were concentrated in three areas; two lay along the hinge-fold zone, and the third within the Parrott-May Day-Idaho fault zone which bounds the dome on the south (Fig. 11).

Ore in the hinge-fold zone was in veins which followed radial or concentric fractures. Veins of the May Day and Idaho mines strike northward; the May Day-Idaho eastward-trending fault zone carries no ore, but the Neglected vein, in the northeast part of the district, strikes eastward and was an important producer. The small, discontinuous fractures inside the horseshoe fold follow also the eastward trend, which appears to be regional and to extend beyond the area of the La Plata dome.

Many La Plata telluride veins are mineralized sheeted zones resembling those of Sunlight, Kirwin, and Silverton. Other veins are mineralized rock breccias; vein matter fills interstices within the rubble and replaces rock fragments to varying degrees. Counterparts of these veins are also at Silverton, Kirwin, and Sunlight. Drusy cavities are common in the veins.

RELATION OF STRUCTURE TO METALLIZATION : Ore deposition at La Plata followed intrusion of the nonporphyritic stocks. Doming which began before or during the epoch of porphyry intrusion, and which persisted through that of plutonic intrusion, was still operative at the time of metallization, because at that time older, mainly radial fractures were reopened, and new fractures were formed with orientation similar to the older breaks. Reopened older fractures and new ones became loci for ore bodies.

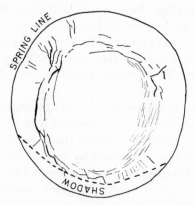

FIGURE 12.—*Experimental dome showing hinge fold*

During this period displacements on radial faults were transferred via concentric faults to nearby radial faults. Such adjacent faulting is typical of doming deformation.

A plausible trunk channel for ore solutions at La Plata is offered by the periphery of the possible buried intrusive plug. The semicircular hinge flexure and fault zone above the top of this suspected plug encloses a cylinder of intensely silicified rock. The outer edge of strong silicification is sharp and suggests structural control of silicification. The controlling structure may well have been the circular fault suggested above, which extended upward above the top of the plug. Such a fault, separating hard silicified rock within it from softer rock without, could furnish the upward continuation above the top of an intrusive plug of a trunk channel provided at depth by the periphery of the plug.

SOURCES FOR LA PLATA : Cross (1899; 1901) ; Eckel (1936; 1949)

RICO, COLORADO

REGIONAL SETTING : The Rico dome, like that of La Plata, lies on the southwest flank of the great San Juan uplift (Pl. 1). The normal dip of the sedimentary beds where undisturbed by the dome is very gently southwestward. This regional dip has been in part reversed on the northeast side of the dome and steepened on the southwest side (Pl. 2).

ROCK FORMATIONS:

Sedimentary Rocks

Age	*Formation*	*Thickness* (Feet)
Upper Cretaceous	Mancos shale	1000
	Dakota sandstone	100–150
Upper Jurassic	McElmo formation;† sandstone and shale	400–1000
	La Plata sandstone†	250–500
Jurassic (?) and Upper Triassic	Dolores formation; "red beds"	400
Permian	Cutler formation; "red beds"	1000
	Rico formation; shale, sandstone	300
Pennsylvanian	Hermosa formation; shale, limestone	1800
Devonian	Ouray limestone	100–300
Cambrian	Ignaciom quartzite	0–200
"Algonkian"	"Uncompahgre formation"; quartzite	?
...	Erosion surface	
"Archean"	Schist	

†The terms "McElmo formation" and "La Plata sandstone" are no longer in use. The McElmo formation and the upper part of the La Plata sandstone are now correlated with the Morrison formation; the lower part of the La Plata sandstone is now called the Entrada sandstone. However, since the source publications on Rico employ the older terminology, it seems best to let it stand. For the same reason, the outdated terms "Algonkian" and "Archean" are retained, in quotation marks.

A monzonite stock has invaded the Rico dome, west of its apex (Pl. 2). Dikes and sills of monzonite porphyry are abundant; most sills have invaded the "red beds" of the Dolores formation.

STRUCTURE: The Rico dome has an average diameter of 13 miles and a rise of 4500 feet, only 700 feet of which is due to intrusion of sills (Cross and Spencer, 1900, p. 105). The ratio of vertical rise to diameter is 1:16, compared to a corresponding ratio for La Plata of 1:14.

The Rico dome, like that of La Plata, is elongated eastward and shows local irregularities in the general quaquaversal attitude of the beds (Pl. 2). The dome is intensely fractured and faulted, especially near its apex. The faults fall into three categories with respect to the domical structure:

(1) Rudely concentric faults which tend to follow the strike of the beds as they swing around the apex of the dome. The upthrown side is toward the domical apex in most of these faults so that the rise of the dome is accentuated by the faulting. Examples: the fault 1 mile northeast of the Johnny Bull mine, the fault 1 mile northwest of the Princeton mine, and that south of Newman Hill. Such faults resemble the rudely concentric faults northwest of the apex of the La Plata dome (Fig. 11).

(2) Faults trending northeastward, eastward, and southeastward from the apical area, and showing a semiradial arrangement like the spokes of a half wheel.

Examples: the northeast fault northeast of the Princeton mine and the diverging faults enclosing a graben, southeast of the Union Carbonate mine.

Many less important radial fractures occur around the circuit of the dome and are especially aboundant along the horseshoe-shaped flexure passing through the Johnny Bull mine which separates evenly dipping beds on the north, west, and southwest flanks of the dome from the platform at the west end of the upper part of the dome.

(3) Faults which parallel the eastward-trending, or major axis of the elongated dome. Examples: the Telegraph Mountain and Nelly Bly faults, and two faults just south of the Nelly Bly.

The Blackhawk, a major fault, falls into none of these groups.

ANALYSIS OF STRUCTURE: The first and principal uplift at Rico was by doming accompanied by fissuring but no faulting according to Cross and Spencer (1900, p. 105-106). The fissures were mainly radial and through them ascended the magma which fed the sills and which solidified as dikes. Fissuring and dike and sill intrusion went on step by step with doming. Doming was completed by the time of the faulting, according to Cross and Spencer, because the sills were contemporaneous with, or even in some cases later than, the doming, and some of the faults cut and displace sills.

There are reasons for doubting that some of the faults are younger than the doming. Radial and concentric fractures form at a very early stage of doming; whether these fractures become faults or not during the doming depends on their orientation and relative size. Radial fractures, normal to the domical contours, separate segments of the dome which have equal tendencies to rise; consequently radial fractures are not likely to become faults unless they join to form a wedge block which loses connection with the swelling dome (Mono wedge at Ophir).

Long concentric fractures, in contrast, may break the dome into blocks which have unequal tendencies to rise. The block toward the apex has a stronger tendency to rise than does that away from it. If such a fracture dips away from the domical apex, it may become a synthetic normal fault aiding the uplift. If it dips toward the apex, stretching of the domed strata may induce the hanging-wall block—that toward the apex—to drop by gravity in the manner of a graben fault (Fig. 1E; Fig. 13, Goldfield).

These fault types are exemplified by the faults on the Rico dome, which have been described. Such faults are typical of the later stages of doming when the dome loses coherence and breaks into blocks.

The elongated Rico dome broke into blocks chiefly in its apical region, which lies toward its steep eastern margin. Analysis of the structure here must await a description of the mineralization because the two are intimately related.

West of its apex the Rico dome is broader and in general more regular; the strata are not broken into blocks but only cut by relatively short fissures. Here uplift took place by flexing and plastic flow of the strata; block faulting took little or no part in the uplift.

METALLIZATION: Most of the Rico production of silver-lead-zinc ore was from a roughly circular area 3 miles in diameter whose center coincides approximately with the apex of the dome. The richest part of this productive area was Newman Hill, about a mile south of the apex of the dome (Pl. 2). The main ore deposits here were mantos and were found in the Pennsylvanian Hermosa Formation and about 400 feet above the base of the Paleozoic series.

This ore zone, called the Enterprise "blanket," underlies several hundred feet of sandstone and directly overlies a thin but persistent limestone bed, the Blanket limestone, one of several such beds intercalated in a shale series which grades to sandstone in depth.

The "blanket" itself, away from ore, consists of a few feet of silty material lying upon the Blanket limestone and mingled with a shale breccia which grades upward into coherent fissile shale a few feet thick, upon which rests the sandstone.

In some places a bed of gypsum occupies the zone of the silty material; where gypsum occurs the overlying shale is unbrecciated. According to Ransome (1901a, p. 295-296) the gypsum once occupied the entire area of the present blanket but was largely dissolved by hydrothermal solutions leaving the silty material as insoluble residue. With removal of the gypsum the overlying shale collapsed and formed the breccia. Collins (1931, p. 416) points out that the shale not only collapsed to form the breccia but was squeezed by deforming forces into openings developing below it.

The Newman Hill "blanket" ores were formed chiefly by replacement of the silty material above the Blanket limestone. The deposits were ribbon-shaped mantos lying directly above fractures in the rocks below the blanket. Although these fractures commonly split into innumerable branches on approaching the blanket from below and almost never extend above the blanket, the mantos follow faithfully the course of the guiding fractures below them.

There are two systems of guide fractures, one whose members strike north-northwestward, the other composed of east-northeastward-trending fractures. The north-northwestward-trending fractures were associated with more important mantos than were fractures of the other system, but carry only barren quartz and pyrite as veins below their mantos. These veins consist of narrow quartz stringers separated by septa of country rock and thus resemble many veins at La Plata, Silverton, Kirwin, and Sunlight; but their structure is now largely obscured by intense intra- and postmineral crushing with gouge seams that extend upward through the blanket.

In contrast, the east-northeastward-trending guide fractures carried ore identical with that of their mantos as much as 200 feet below the mantos, and these veins were frozen to their walls and showed crustified banding of quartz, rhodochrosite, and ore minerals and a string of druses down the center. Postmineral faulting was absent.

Ore bodies somewhat similar to the mantos of Newman Hill occur in the Union Carbonate mine to the east and in the Princeton mine on the north flank of the dome (Pl. 2).

The radial fractures in the western two-thirds of the dome (Christina, Cow-drey, and many other vein fractures) carry unbanded quartz and pyrite, like the vein matter of the north-northwest "feeders" of Newman Hill; but these western veins did not undergo intramineral or postmineral shattering.

RELATION OF STRUCTURE TO METALLIZATION: The key to the relation lies in Newman Hill, which is on the south flank of a stubby eastward-trending anticline which plunges at both ends and is superimposed like a turret upon the main Rico dome (Pl. 2).

The east-northeastward-trending fractures of Newman Hill parallel the axis of the anticline; the north-northwestward-trending fractures are perpendicular to it.

Figure 1A shows tensional faults in a plate bent around a horizontal axis; Figure 1B shows the orientation of similar faults (or fissures) where the axis plunges. Figure 1C shows tensional faults or fissures produced by bending of an anticlinal axis ("cross joints").

Figure 1F shows the relation between fractures produced by symmetrical doming under vertical force and those attending the formation of an elongated dome or doubly plunging anticline, also the result of vertical force. With a rising and expanding dome, stretching is radial and produces concentric fractures, and is also concentric, producing radial fractures (left-hand sketch, Fig. 1F).

Suppose now the dome to be bisected and the resulting half domes pulled apart to form a doubly plunging anticline. The ends of the new structure retain their domical characteristics, their radial fractures, and segments of a concentric frac-ture once continuous around the dome (right-hand sketch). The new structure grows, however, not by doming from a focal point but by bending of its axis convexly upward (Fig. 1B, 1C). Hence the *east* and *west* segments of the former concentric fracture, which dipped inward, like a cone sheet, toward the center of the dome (Fig. 1E) become two arcuate cross joints, dipping eastward and west-ward respectively, and lying normal to the bent axis of the anticline (Fig. 1C).

The newly made central part of the structure becomes an arch, and the north and south segments of the former concentric fracture are straightened-out longi-tudinal fractures which dip inward (Fig. 1A). Where these fractures are normal faults, a graben along the crest of the arch is produced.

Where the arch merges with the half dome at either end the longitudinal frac-tures bend outward, trumpet-fashion, to join the nearest radial fracture (Fig. 1F, 1B). Compare Figure 1F with Figure 3D, showing the Rhenish and Nubian-Arabian shields.

If the axis of the central arch is bowed upward, continuing the bow of its plunging ends, cross joints may form which lie normal to the bent axis and which therefore dip like the arcuate northward-trending faults in the right-hand sketch of Figure 1F or like the cross joints in the plunging portion of Figure 1C.

Thus, where a symmetrical dome is (analytically) elongated, concentric frac-tures become in part longitudinal fractures, in part arcuate cross joints. Radial fractures remain so at the plunging ends of the anticline but merge with longitudinal fractures where the half domes merge with the connecting arch.

The doubly plunging anticline superimposed upon the eastern portion of the Rico dome resembles Figure 1F. The Nellie Bly fault and the faults south of it are longitudinal faults along the anticlinal axis. The graben between the Nellie Bly and Telegraph Mountain faults flares trumpet-fashion down the eastern nose of the anticline. The graben wedge southeast of the Union Carbonate mine resembles the Mono wedge at Ophir. Other radial fractures cut the semicircular western nose of the anticline.

The Blackhawk fault is neither a longitudinal nor a cross fracture and is therefore anomolous with respect to the anticline. The fracture which formed the Canyon fault at Ophir was also anomolous, in a sense, because it originated as a cross joint on the Ophir anticline and not in response to the forces which produced the dome. Displacement on the Blackhawk is at a maximum at the crest of the uplift and decreases in all directions away from the crest; this is also the case with the Canyon fault.

Displacement on the Rico faults antedated the mineralization. By the time of metallization, therefore, the major features of the Rico dome, including the superimposed anticline, were in existence; but the anticline seems to have been but little fractured until a short time before ore formation started. Collins believes that the north-northwestward-trending cross joints were created before the east-northeastward-trending longitudinal fractures, and that the cross joints were loci for minor fault movements through and beyond the period of mineralization. In terms of the mechanics postulated above, this late deformation cycle started with upbowing of the anticlinal axis to produce the cross joints. Continued upbowing instigated persistent movement along these fractures.

Soon after upbending of the anticlinal axis began, beds of the anticline were stretched in two directions. While the axis continued to bend convexly upward, flexing of the beds around the anticlinal axis was suddenly resumed; this flexing was sharp enough to produce longitudinal fractures (east-northeastward-trending system). Unlike the persistent upbowing of the axis, flexing around the axis was a single brief episode because according to Collins the east-northeastward-trending fissures opened just in time to catch the surge of rich ore and were not disturbed thereafter.

The structurally weak blanket of Newman Hill acted as a tectonic insulator, like a layer of soft grease between two brittle blocks under strain. Sandstone lies above the thin shale series of the blanket, and the shale series also grades downward into sandstone. The cross joints and longitudinal tension fissures just described opened in the competent sandstone below the shale, but they weakened and branched going upward and were stopped by the soft shale of the blanket and especially by the loose silt in which the mantos formed.

Mineralization began soon after upward bending of the anticlinal axis got under way. During the ore surge movements on the cross joints plus bed faulting along the weak layer of residual silt in the blanket enlarged and extended openings in the shale, breccia, and silt. These movements and the enlargement of the openings guided and localized ore deposition by fluids rising along the north-northwest-ward-trending cross joints and penetrating the blanket where they deposited ore by a combination of replacement and open-space filling. The ore solutions were "sucked up" into the blanket to form mantos. No ore was deposited in the feed-ing fissures, because owing to the permeable nature of the blanket overlying the feeders no "damming" action to back the solutions down into the feeders took place. After formation of the mantos renewed movement opened the feeders to receive late barren quartz, which was shattered by still later movements.

In the case of the east-northeastward-trending or longitudinal feeders there was but a single gaping of the fissure walls to receive vein matter of the rich ore surge. These movements created much less shattering of the weak blanket than did the recurrent minor fault movements along the north-northwestward-trending feeders. Ascending solutions found few openings in the blanket above the feeder. They formed inferior mantos and backed down the feeder, depositing ore that sealed it against further movement.

The Newman Hill feeders and mantos are in the central arch connecting the two half domes of the plunging anticline. The Union Carbonate blanket ore bodies occurred in the eastern half dome. The feeders there are radial fractures which parallel those of the graben wedge southeast of the mine. The feeders resemble the radial fractures in the right-hand sketch of Figure 1F. They veer northwest-ward toward a westerly strike which is that of the longitudinal fractures of the central arch.

The fact that the radial veins around the western portion of the Rico dome resemble in their mineralogy the veins in the cross joints of Newman Hill sug-gests that these vein fissures, like the cross joints, opened too late to receive the rich ore.

SOURCES FOR RICO: Collins (1931); Cross and Spencer (1900); Hubbell (1927); Ransome (1901a)

GOLDFIELD, NEVADA

REGIONAL SETTING: This late Tertiary gold district is near the southwest edge of the Great Basin (Pl. 1). Although the axis of the geosyncline traversing Nevada in Paleozoic time passed not far east of the Goldfield area, the crystalline basement is now elevated in a series of structural highs, most of which trend roughly northward. Goldfield lies above a platform in the basement between two marked structural highs.

ROCK FORMATIONS: Tertiary latite, rhyolite, dacite, and andesite extrusives rest upon Cambrian shale intruded, before the volcanism, by alaskite. The pre-volcanic surface was one of low relief.

STRUCTURE: The dominant structure is that of a dome about 6 miles in diame-ter (Fig. 13). The ratio of vertical rise to diameter seems to be on the order of 1:20, so that the dome is somewhat flatter than those of Rico and La Plata. Several satellitic domes lie on the southwest flank of the main dome.

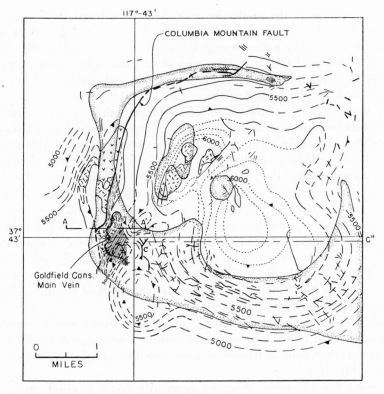

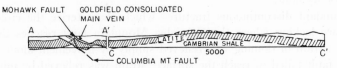

FIGURE 13.—*Structural map and section, Goldfield district, Nevada*

A remarkable concentric normal fault, the Columbia Mountain fault, follows the structural contours of the dome in the northwest quadrant. The fault dips inward toward the apex of the dome. The fault completes a belt of intense minor fracturing and alteration which almost encircles the dome, but in the arc occupied by the fault minor fracturing is almost lacking.

The fractures within this annular belt fall into a concentric and a radial set, but concentric fractures predominate.

Mine workings in the productive area on the southwest flank of the dome (Fig. 13) have shown that the many irregular fractures at and near the surface coalesce at depth into a few strong concentric fractures which dip, like the Columbia Mountain fault, toward the apex of the dome. One such fracture is the Goldfield Consolidated Main vein (Fig. 13, Plan and Section A-C'); several more are shown in the detailed section of Searls (1948, Pl. II).

The uniform course of the Columbia Mountain fault over most of its known length is broken in the productive area by two sharp southwest jogs. The Goldfield Consolidated Main vein lies in the prolongation of the Columbia Mountain fault south of the first southwestward jog, but unlike the smooth course of the Columbia Mountain fault north of the jog the Main vein has a sinuous course (Fig. 13).

ANALYSIS OF STRUCTURE: The fact that the discontinuous fractures near the surface in the productive area merge at depth into fewer but more regular and continuous fractures makes it reasonable to assume that this holds for the entire fracture zone encircling the Goldfield dome. In that case the discontinuous fractures throughout the zone coalesce at depth into a group of ring faults which dip toward the apex of the dome. The strong, continuous alteration, and the ore deposits, both of which are confined to the circular belt of fractures, suggest a continuous solution channel at depth.

Such a continuous concentric break or zone of breaks would resemble the fractures occupied by the cone sheets of western Scotland, and Sunlight. Cone-sheet fractures originate as tension fissures caused by radial stretching of a doming plate (Fig. 1E).

Whereas the Columbia Mountain concentric break probably encircles the dome at depth, it reaches the surface only in the northwest quadrant. Here it broke the dome into two blocks. Had the uplifting force been centered sharply beneath the apex of the dome, reverse faulting might have taken place along this break. At Goldfield, however, the uplifting force was distributed throughout the domed area. (Figure 13, Section A-C', shows that the west flank of the dome in the footwall of the Columbia Mountain fault has been strongly uplifted.) Under such conditions the hanging-wall block, toward the apex of the dome, dropped as a normal gravity fault.

The abundant discontinuous fractures which characterize the circular zone elsewhere are lacking where the Columbia Mountain fault reaches the surface because the strain of doming was relieved simply by movement along the fault. Where the fault failed to reach the surface, strain was relieved by minor radial and concentric fracturing in which concentric fractures dominate because they reflect the master fracturing below.

The discontinuous fractures in the circular belt suggest deformation of brittle rock, but they lie now within a zone of rock softened by hydrothermal alteration which would deform today by flow rather than fracture. Plainly the fractures formed before the rock was softened. The belt of alteration coincides with that of fracturing which suggests that the softening solutions rose along the fractures which offered a fine-scale mesh of channels from which to permeate the rock.

The softening process consisted of alunitization and kaolinization and was followed by silicification which formed the striking Goldfield "ledges." Silicification of the walls of channel fractures formed the underlying, tabular "keels" of these ledges, whereas toward the surface silica spread outward from its channels to produce the nontabular and highly irregular "blow-outs," the ledges themselves.

Blankets of gouge surround the brittle ledges and are found throughout the soft matrix which flowed under stress, whereas the ledges could not flow but had to fracture. They were repeatedly shattered and even pulverized in places.

The exaggerated tendency to fracture shown by brittle bodies encased in soft material is discussed by Balk (1937, p. 32) :

"Experiments have been made by A. Föppl, E. Seidl and Hans Cloos. Tear cracks, or tension joints formed, if a block was squeezed so that its compressed surfaces were free to move at right angles to the direction of maximum compression. . . . The better the compressed block was lubricated . . . the better is the development of the tension joints. The more the compressed block and its surrounding soft material differ in brittleness the sooner the cracks appear."

If the solutions that softened the rock ascended the postulated ring fault dipping inward, the softened body had the shape of a thick cone sheet. Under doming, compression and shortening would occur in directions normal to the doming strata; since the cone sheet lies also normal to the strata, these directions correspond, in terms of mathematics, to elements of the cone. Tension and stretching would operate in two directions, one radial with respect to the dome and normal to the surface of the cone, the other concentric both with respect to the apex of the dome and to the axis of the cone. In other words, the "cone sheet" would tend to shorten vertically but would thicken, and its diameter in horizontal section would increase.

Under such deformation the soft material would flow, but the brittle ledges would shatter.

Mine development in the productive area on the southwest flank of the dome has thrown light on the mechanics of deformation there. The Goldfield Consolidated Main vein fracture is genetically connected to the Columbia Mountain fault.

". . . the lode-like Goldfield Consolidated vein is almost exactly in the prolongation of the plane of the Columbia Mountain fault north of this [sudden westward] turn. It evidently represents a sheer zone or series of cracks, formed in extenso, as it were, of the northerly part of the great fault, without sharing appreciably in the movement that occurred on the fault itself," (Searls, 1948, p. 19).

Movement on the Columbia Mountain fault was normal, and so was that on its offspring, the Goldfield Consolidated vein fracture; but dip slip on the latter was slight.

The Combination ledge is a vertical dip split extending upward from the hanging-wall side of the flat-dipping Goldfield Consolidated Main vein and paralleling that vein in strike. Where it leaves the Main vein the split is a vein also, but above it expands to a fat, irregular ledge and resembles the ore-bearing dip splits in the hanging wall of the Comstock main lode (Ransome, 1909a, Pl. XVII, XVIII, p. 155).

The main vein in depth follows the dacite-latite contact (Fig. 13, Section A-C'). Just where the Combination dip split leaves the Main vein, the contact is warped into an anticlinal wrinkle.

The Columbia Mountain fault, in the area of its two westward jogs, is also an irregular surface. Underground exploration by Searls found three vertical dip splits in the hanging wall of the fault. One of them was a wide vein carrying rich ore. This vein could "actually be seen departing from the low-grade pyritic mineralization of the Columbia Mountain fault, like a branch from a tree trunk" (Searls, 1948, p. 21). This dip split leaves the Columbia Mountain fault at a pronounced irregularity in the surface.

"Feather joints" (E. Cloos, 1932; Hills, 1941, p. 122-124) are acute-angle branches of major fractures. They are so called because, with respect to the fault or fracture from which they spring, they are arranged like the barbs of a feather with respect to its shaft. The acute angle between the branch and the main fracture points in the direction of relative movement (or tendency toward movement) of the blocks on either side of the main fracture.

The origin of feather joints has been suggested by Wisser (1939, p. 318). Where faulting occurs

"Completely free movement of one fault block past another involves no strain in the parts of the blocks adjoining the fault. The case is that of one brick shoved past an adjoining brick . . . with no pressing of the bricks together as they slide. But if high friction opposes the movement, a given force will displace one block with respect to the other less than with free movement. The parts of the blocks next to the fault will be intensely strained in the effort of the force to overcome the high friction opposing the movement. A shearing stress is set up and the rock on both sides of the fault is stretched in a direction crossing the fault obliquely. . . . If this tensional stress exceeds the tensional breaking strength of the deformed rock, 'feather joints' or tension fissures form perpendicular to the direction of stretching."

Actual fault displacements need not take place to produce feather joints because as movement is impeded the shearing strain increases.

These considerations suggest that the steep dip splits off the flat-dipping main fractures in the Goldfield productive area are feather joints; they are oriented to conform with normal-fault movements and they leave their parent fractures where these are locally distorted in a manner to hinder fault movements and strain the adjoining rock.

The Columbia Mountain fault in its straight northern segment was adapted toward free-slipping fault movements with a minimum of strain in the fault walls. No feather joints are known there.

The origin of the irregularities in the Columbia Mountain fault and the Goldfield Main vein is not clear. Searls (1948, p. 14) attributes the main jog in the Columbia Mountain fault to a combination of a sharp bend to the west and westerly displacement by "subsequent east-west faults." Such eastward-trending faults would lie radially with respect to the main dome.

Radial and concentric fractures often form simultaneously during doming. The Columbia Mountain fault is only one of several concentric fractures in this area (Main vein, Clermont, Sheets-Ish, and others). All originated as tension fissures; but, as doming continued, the strongest, the Columbia Mountain fault, may have acted as a normal gravity fault. It could do so without complications as far south as the first important radial break it encountered, and here it may have ended.

On reaching the break, the Columbia Mountain fault would tend to cross the radial break and extend itself southward. It succeeded only in producing the Main vein fracture, formed "in extenso . . . of the northerly part of the great fault," to quote again the analysis of Searls.

The Columbia Mountain fault movement then may have followed the eastward-trending radial break westward until a concentric fracture south of the radial break was encountered; the concentric fracture would then become the southern extension of the Columbia Mountain fault.

Such an origin can hardly apply to the wavy Main vein. Figure 13 shows two satellitic domes, separated by a trough, in the area of the Main vein. The vein follows roughly the structural contours of the northern dome but bulges westward in the basin, where it ends. These structural relations suggest that the Main vein may have been folded by the rise of the northern dome and sag of the basin. Such folding, if it occurred, presumably preceded the slight normal-fault movements on the vein fracture which were associated with formation of the steep feather joints. That faulting could well have been connected with rise of the northern minor dome because the Main vein fracture stands in the same relation to that dome as the Columbia Mountain fault does to the main dome.

An en echelon southeast prolongation of the Main vein fracture looks like a radial fracture on the southern satellite dome. If so, it bolsters the notion that these minor domes were forming during fracturing and faulting in this area.

METALLIZATION: Most of the Goldfield silica ledges are barren of gold; but the upper and principal portion of nearly all the ore bodies lay within such ledges. Most production was from the small area on the southwest flank of the dome discussed above (cross-hatched area, Fig. 13).

Primary ore consisted of native gold in fine-grained quartz and very minor amounts of pyrite, sphalerite, and complex sulfides of antimony, arsenic, bismuth, and tellurium.

I have shown that the irregular ledges or "blowouts" commonly possess a tabular "keel" of silica on their lower sides. In barren ledges the silica keel disappears with depth and is absent from the soft matrix enclosing the ledges. Mine workings show that productive ledges have maintained connection with such major fractures as the Main vein by downward persistence of their silica keels.

RELATION OF STRUCTURE TO METALLIZATION: Both productive and barren ledges were fractured persistently; fracturing of productive ledges took place before, during, and after formation of the ore shoots. The silica keels maintaining connection between productive ledges and trunk solution channels at depth were shattered and kept permeable by slight movements which triggered the influx of ore-bearing solutions up the keel and into the "blowout" above, which was shattered also to permit entry and deposition of ore. Ideal conditions for ore localization were supplied by a loose, open shattering unaccompanied by any movement tending to compact the shattered material. Apparently even this kind of shattering, however, unless it took place at the precise time of ore invasion, localized no ore.

The barren ledges, although they shattered like the ore ledges, lacked continuous keels beneath them to serve as channels for ore solutions. The soft matrix prevented access of such solutions.

It is evident that the trunk channels for solutions that softened the rock were identical with those that silicified it and with those that brought in the ore at Goldfield. According to Searls (1948, p. 21) the trunk channel was the ring fault or zone of ring faults of which the Columbia Mountain fault is a part.

The Columbia Mountain fault, south of its westward jog, fed ore to the three dip-split feather-joint veins found by Searls. Ore solutions which used the Goldfield Consolidated Main vein as a channel probably reached it via the Columbia Mountain fault and left that fault at its westward jog. The Main vein in turn fed ore to the Combination feather joint in its hanging wall, up which the solutions moved to the ledge, where they deposited their load. The Jumbo and January ledges were supplied with ore in the same way. Some ore ledges were not fed by steep feather-joint branches of the Main vein but were fed directly by concentric fractures which parallel the Main vein in strike and dip (Red, Top, Mohawk, Clermont, and Sheets-Ish ledges).

Whereas conditions at Goldfield are in some respects unique, tectonic control of ore deposition there by persistent doming during metallization was not essentially different from that manifested at Rico, La Plata, Silverton, and other districts associated with domes.

SOURCES FOR GOLDFIELD: E. F. Lambert (1948, unpublished report); Locke (1912); Ransome (1909a); Searls (1948)

LONGITUDINAL AND TRANSVERSE FRACTURE PATTERNS

DEFINITIONS

LONGITUDINAL FRACTURES: Fractures which strike parallel to the axis of an anticline or elongate dome. Where the anticline plunges, longitudinal fractures may diverge or flare down the nose (Figs. 1B, F).

TRANSVERSE FRACTURES OR "CROSS JOINTS": Fractures which strike normal to the axis of an anticline or elongate dome (Fig. 1C).

ORIGIN

Epi-anticlinal fractures.—Longitudinal and transverse fractures are so typically associated with doubly plunging minor anticlines of the Rocky Mountain petroleum region that they are called by Irwin epi-anticlinal (1926, p. 113); he believes that they formed concurrently with the folding and in part, at least, as a result of stretching of the upfolded strata (1926, p. 122-123).

Epi-anticlinal fractures are not limited to the Rocky Mountain petroleum region of Wyoming and Montana but occur throughout the world. The explanation of the origin of isolated doubly plunging minor anticlines will account for their associated fracture patterns as well.

McCoy (1934) believes that the main component of relative movement which produced the isolated anticlines of the Mid-Continent petroleum region was vertical because they show no relation in time or space to the great orogenic epochs and regions supposedly associated with tangential compression by crustal shortening, and because, if tangential stress were transmitted over the great distances from such orogenic regions to the mid-continent minor anticlines, the relatively weak rocks that would have to transmit the stress would be permanently deformed and show evidence of flowage. This is nowhere the case (1934, p. 613).

The structures with which much of the oil in the Rocky Mountain and Mid-Continent fields is associated range from nearly symmetrical domes through elongate domes to relatively minor anticlines which plunge and disappear at both ends. These structures are spaced in a disconnected manner, although sometimes with some apparent system, and, significantly, are not associated with corresponding synclines. They have the appearance of what German geologists call "boils" or "tumours," or what the writer has called "upfolds." A few typical examples will be examined.

Anticlines with longitudinal fracture patterns.—The Salt Valley anticline, Utah (Fig. 14A, from Harrison, 1927, Fig. 9), lies along the northwest prolongation of the Paradox-La Sal uplift. Harrison (1927) believes it was formed by lateral and upward migration of salt and anhydrite under pressure of superincumbent rock; this is the prevailing theory for the origin of salt domes. Regardless of how much the salt may have moved laterally toward the area of the anticline, the salt moved upward to create the anticline by differential vertical movements as a true upfold.

53

The anticline carries an axial graben which flares or widens down its plunging nose. The faults that bound the graben originated as tension fissures during arching, and the graben block dropped as a loose keystone as arching continued. Section A-A′ of Figure 14A shows that arching, or flexing around the anticlinal axis, was severe.

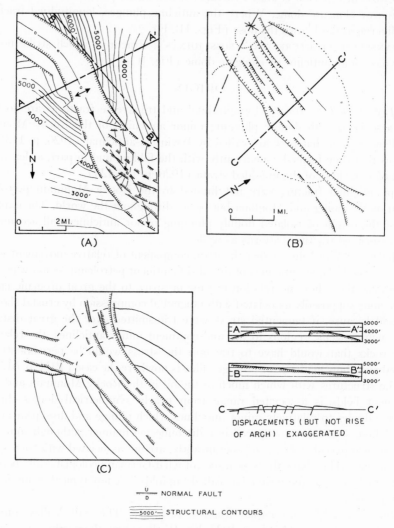

FIGURE 14.—*Anticlines with longitudinal fracture patterns*

Cross joints on anticlinal upfolds are often oriented normal to the axis and seem to have formed by bending of the axis (Fig. 1C). Section B-B′ shows that the axis of the Salt Valley anticline is not bent but plunges uniformly northwest. The anticline carries no cross joints.

Figure 14B after Irwin (1926, Fig. 7) shows an elongate dome in New

Mexico which carries an axial graben at one end where the dome grades into the adjoining undeformed region. At the other end the dome abuts against a transverse syncline; this end of the dome is constricted, and no flaring of the graben takes place. Figure 14C illustrates an experiment by H. Cloos (1939, Fig. 22). A clay cake was upfolded into a plunging anticline by inflation of a rubber bag beneath it. The flanks of the fold were entirely unconfined. The axial graben that developed flares outward down the plunging nose, and radial fractures develop also on the nose.

Anticlines with transverse fracture patterns.—These are especially common in the Rocky Mountain petroleum field. The Big Muddy anticline (Pl. 1; Fig. 15,

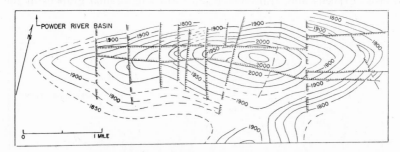

FIGURE 15.—*Big Muddy anticline, Wyoming*

after Espach and Nichols, 1941) lies on the south slope of the Powder River basin and trends eastward, parallel to the structural contours of the basin. Unlike the Salt Valley anticline in Utah, the Big Muddy anticline is broken by cross fractures as well as by an axial graben. The anticlinal axis is bowed upward as the structural contours show. Nearly all the cross fractures dip eastward, but all but two are in the western portion where the axis plunges westward. These western fractures are therefore oriented normal to the axis (Fig. 1C).

The Salt Creek anticline lies on the southwest slope of the Powder River basin, near the Big Muddy anticline. It trends northwestward and, like the Big Muddy structure, parallels the structural contours of the basin. Figure 16 (after Thom and Spieker, 1931) shows Teapot dome, which is superimposed on the larger Salt Creek anticline. The elongate Teapot dome is overturned to the southwest up the slope of the basin.

The elongate dome or doubly plunging anticline is broken by cross faults which strike about normal to its axis. Maximum displacement on these faults occurs on the crest of the structure, and displacements disappear down the flanks. Thom and Spieker (1913, p. 19) believe that these breaks developed during elevation of the anticline and upbending of its axis, but ascribe them to compressive stress acting toward the northeast and upward against the steep southwest flank of the anticline.

The nature of the fracture pattern opposes this theory. The largest cross graben traversing the apex of Teapot dome flares outward down the steep southwest flank. Such flaring indicates that the flanks of the anticline were free and not confined by lateral compression (Fig. 14C).

Nearly all the cross breaks on Teapot dome dip toward the highest point on its bowed-up axis and are therefore oriented normal to the axis (Fig. 1C). They are tension breaks caused by longitudinal arching. The only exceptions to this dip pattern are furnished by the four cross grabens which dropped as keystone wedges.

The Salt Creek anticline carries longitudinal as well as cross grabens (longitudinal grabens not shown in Fig. 16). Where tangential compression bows up competent beds, longitudinal grabens might form, but the strata here are relatively weak. In such rocks, only upfolding can stretch a structure longitudinally to form cross grabens and, transversely, to form longitudinal grabens at the same time.

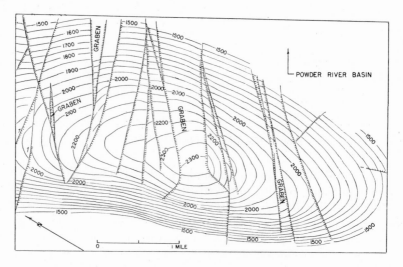

FIGURE 16.—*Teapot dome, Wyoming*

Fissuring and faulting on anticlinal upfolds of brittle material.—The origin of grabens on anticlinal upfolds has been discussed, but there is another type of faulting characteristic of such folds. If longitudinal normal faults on such structures dip conjugately toward the axial plane (Fig. 1A), or if transverse normal faults lie normal to the anticlinal axis (Fig. 1C), the faulting may be of the antithetic type (H. Cloos, 1928; Hills, 1941, p. 65).

An antithetic fault is one genetically associated with a larger movement, but by its displacement it opposes that movement. An anticlinal upfold of brittle material is cut into blocks by longitudinal normal faults whose dip is inward toward the axis of arching and normal to the dip of the arched strata (Fig. 1A). These faults originate as tension fissures created by bending of the strata around the axis. If the tensional strain continues it may be relieved by rotating or toppling of the blocks between the fissures down the flanks of the arch. The fissures thus become faults whose displacement is due entirely to rotation of the blocks which they bound. Although these faults are results of the major movement producing the arching they tend to lessen the rise of the arch and are antithetic.

Figure 17A is a cross section through Elden Mountain, Arizona (Robinson, 1913, Fig. 23, Section C-C'). Here viscous dacite uplifted sediments into an irregular dome. Concentric tension fissures broke the brittle plate into blocks which tended to overturn downslope and produced antithetic faults.

The Antelope, Nevada, mining district lies on the east flank of an anticline. Antithetic faulting of brittle rhyolite flows is shown in Figure 17B (after Schrader, 1913, Fig. 14).

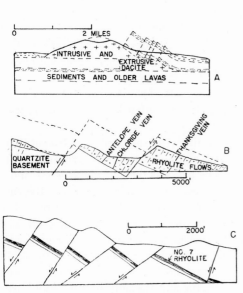

FIGURE 17.—*Sections to illustrate antithetic faulting*

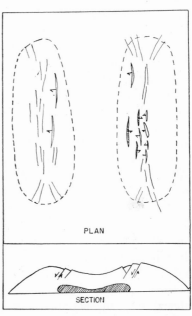

FIGURE 18.—*Experiment on anticlines due to sag*

Part of the structure at Bullfrog, Nevada, is shown in Figure 17C (after Emmons and Garrey, 1910, Fig. 11, who concluded that the most likely mechanism to explain the step faulting was that of simultaneous faulting and tilting).

Flow and faulting on anticlinal upfolds of plastic material.—Where soft, plastic, or incompetent rock is domed, radial and concentric fractures are nearly always faults, whereas they originate as tension fissures in brittle material. Radial faults are not vertical, as in brittle material, but dip initially at about 60° in either direction and make up conjugate sets of "shear planes" (Parker and McDowell, 1951, p. 2086; E. Cloos, 1955, p. 248 and Pl. 5, fig. 2). With continued doming these faults flatten almost to the horizontal.

Where soft material is upfolded into an anticline, longitudinal and transverse fractures are also always faults which can dip either way (Fig. 18). Continued arching flattens the dips. Whereas upfolding of brittle material tends to produce master fissures, upfolding of soft material produces many discontinuous minor faults (Fig. 18).

Soft material behaves differently from brittle during upfolding because it tends to flow—*i.e.*, to change shape without loss of cohesion, without splitting like brittle material, into discrete blocks which thereafter deform as units and not internally. Many materials seem to flow by development of an extremely fine-scale network of planar or curved surfaces which in cross section are identical with the Lüders lines associated with deformation of mild steel, and which cross one another at angles from acute to obtuse. Rotation of the extremely thin plates between members of each set of surfaces accomplishes the flow (Hills, 1941, p. 33-35, Fig. 16). Each slip surface functions as an antithetic fault of microscopic displacement. Burbank (1941, p. 163-167) invokes this mechanism to explain flow of rock rendered soft by alteration into the Red Mountain sag at Silverton.

Actually these conjugate slip surfaces are equally developed only at the start of deformation; as deformation proceeds certain surfaces become faults with notable displacements whereas the surrounding material may continue to flow by rotation of slip surfaces with microscopic displacements. That is why the faults in the scale-model experiments of Parker and McDowell flatten in dip as doming proceeds.

An experiment by Ernst Cloos, at which the writer assisted, is pertinent here. A rubber bag placed on a table was inflated, and a clay cake was molded over its upper surface to form an elongate dome. The bag was then slowly deflated, and a central basin was produced (Fig. 18). The clay was unstrained before the sag, but as sag proceeded longitudinal fractures appeared on the anticlines on either side of the basin. The fractures flared outward on each nose of the anticlines. The fracture pattern was nearly identical with that of the experiment of Figure 14C in which a rubber bag was inflated to form a plunging anticline. Sag of the basin stretched the clay on the crests and on the basinward flanks of the anticlines, even though the anticlinal areas remained stationary and the only positive movement involved was the sag which formed the basin.

The longitudinal fractures were discontinuous conjugate faults; one set dipped toward the basin, the other into the anticlines. Flow of clay downslope toward the basin rotated and flattened faults dipping into the anticlines; faulting on this set was antithetic because their normal displacements decreased the rise of the anticlinal arches. Faults dipping toward the basin were not rotated. They were what H. Cloos has termed synthetic faults because the drop of their hanging walls contributed directly to the sag. In positive uplifts normal faults dipping away from the anticlinal axis contribute directly to the uplift. They are not rotated during uplift and are likewise synthetic faults.

In the experiment, displacements on the short faults of either type reached their maxima at the midpoint and decreased to zero at each end.

Folds in the cover caused by faults in the basement.—Thom (1923) shows that asymmetric elongate domes in central Montana have their steeper flanks above faults in the basement (Fig. 19A; Thom's diagram has been slightly modified to show folds produced by synthetic faulting on the flank of an uplift). Figure 19B shows folds in the cover produced by antithetic faults on the flank of an uplift. Here the steeper flanks of the folds face upslope, instead of downslope as with synthetic normal faulting. Figure 19C shows folds produced by synthetic reverse faults. The steeper limb faces downslope as with synthetic normal faulting, but the folds tend to overturn more sharply downslope.

Origin of minor anticlines on slopes between basins and uplifts.—The experiment of Figure 18 and the ideas of Thom may apply to minor anticlines associated with the basins and uplifts of the Big Horn region in northern Wyoming (Pl. 1). The tectonic history of this region resembles that of the experiment of

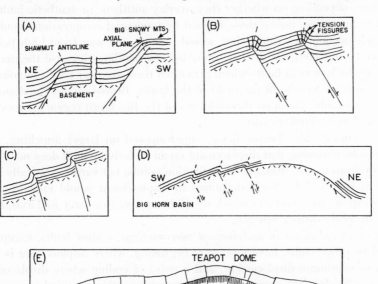

FIGURE 19.—*Folds in the cover caused by faults in the basement,
and diagram to explain dips of cross faults on Teapot dome*

Figure 18 because the basins there were sites of sag over long periods. Unlike the experiment, in the Big Horn region much of the sag took place concurrently with uplift of the ranges bordering the basins, but this only increased the strain in the hinge zones between basins and uplifts and does not invalidate the comparison.

The slopes of the major basins and, conversely, those of their adjoining uplifts are studded with minor anticlines, among which are the Salt Creek and Big Muddy anticlines. According to Ball (1921) these "basin upfolds" are of two types; the steeper limb of the commoner is toward the nearest uplift, and in the less usual type the steeper limb faces the adjacent basin.

These folds cannot be explained by tangential compression transmitted from one direction or another; the sediments were too weak to transmit such compression; synclines corresponding to the anticlines are lacking, and on the flank of an uplift some minor anticlines are overturned upslope, others downslope. The mechanics outlined above seem to suggest an origin for these parasitic folds.

Major elongated uplifts, such as that of the Big Horn, may be considered anticlines of the first order. Whereas the core of the Big Horn uplift is Precambrian granite, its flanks are for the most part schist (Ernst and Hans Cloos, 1934). Such material, like the clay in the experiment cited, would be likely to flow when deformed and to develop abundant discontinuous antithetic and synthetic faults on the slope between the sagging basin and the adjacent rising mass. Anticlines of the second order might develop in the stratified sedimentary cover above the basement schist (Fig. 19D), and they would be overturned upslope or downslope, depending on whether they overlay antithetic or synthetic faults.

These anticlines, unlike those formed by tangential compression, would have no complementary synclines; they would plunge each way from high points on their crests and merge with their unfolded surroundings because the maximum throws of the basement faults which generated them are near their midpoints, and throws decrease to zero at each end of the faults. Bowed-up anticlinal axes give rise to cross faults which on the anticlines of the Big Horn region are more common than longitudinal fractures.

Local cupolas like Teapot dome, superimposed on larger anticlines, can be explained by assuming that displacement on an underlying fault does not decrease smoothly from its maximum to its extinction points, but varies erratically as suggested in Figure 19E. Such variations in displacement would explain also the varying dip of cross fractures which would lie normal to a wavy fold axis, and not to one smoothly convex upward.

Origin of anticlines in undeformed surroundings.—Most faults, except those blocked by other faults, have a point of beginning, where displacement is zero, a stretch of maximum displacement, and a point of ending where displacement is again zero. Such faults, occurring in a basement beneath a stratified cover whether on the flank of an uplift or in flat-lying terrain, might be expected to produce folds in their cover similar to those described. On the Colorado Plateau, strata adjoining asymmetric elongate domes such as the San Rafael Swell and the Monument, Defiance, and Zuni uplifts lie flat. It has long been suspected that such folds are reflections in the cover of faults in the basement.

Faults in the basement may not have been the sole cause of many of these asymmetric upfolds. Magma rising up the basement fault and spreading laterally along the strike of the fault beneath soft strata may have added to the doming. According to Thom (1923, p. 9), the Big Elk, Little Elk, and Shawmut elongate asymmetric domes probably have laccolithic cores.

Symmetrical anticlines, in contrast, and especially those rising from undeformed terrain, are less suggestive of basement faults beneath them. Their form suggests rather rise of an underlying mass, which may be salt, in the Salt Valley and similar anticlines, or magma, in the case of many anticlines associated with mining districts.

Many mining districts in western North America lie on isolated anticlines in

Tertiary lava flows which, where they surround the anticline, are flat lying and undeformed. The volcanic rocks behaved in a brittle manner under deformation so that tension fissures accompanied an early stage of the upfolding which created the anticline. Often the tension fissures tapped a magma reservoir, in which case magma ascended them and filled them with dikes. Such dike-filled fissures seldom became faults, but with continued uplift new fissures formed. Strong fissures on each side of the anticlinal axis and dipping toward it in many cases became faults bounding an axial graben whereas fissures farther down the flanks and dipping into the anticline turned into antithetic faults.

One suspects that such isolated upfolds in volcanic rocks, and especially those containing abundant dikes and stocks, owe their formation and that of their fracture pattern to rise of magma at depth. Large uplifts of this type may carry anticlines of the second order on their flanks, like those on the Big Horn uplift. These satellitic anticlines may have formed above faults associated with later stages of uplift, as those on the Big Horn uplift are supposed to have done.

Isolated anticlines in undeformed surroundings commonly show longitudinal fractures, whereas in upfolds on the flanks of major uplifts cross fractures seem to dominate.

Mining districts on upfolds with dominant longitudinal fractures will first be described.

MINING DISTRICTS ASSOCIATED
WITH ANTICLINES
CREEDE, COLORADO

REGIONAL SETTING: Creede lies 40 miles east of Silverton in the center of the San Juan volcanic field and on the eastern flank of the San Juan uplift (Pl. 1). The volcanic field contains a number of grabens, one of which forms the structural setting of the Creede mining district. In a general way the graben axes parallel the northeastern border of the Colorado Plateau and form a belt convex to the northeast.

The San Juan volcanic rocks are almost surrounded by Precambrian crystalline rocks exposed at elevations as high as, or higher than, that of the volcanic rocks which rest directly on the crystalline rocks or upon thin remnants of Paleozoic or Mesozoic sedimentary rocks. Such relations accord with the persistently positive role played by the San Juan region.

ROCK FORMATIONS: (Miocene?)

Formation	Thickness (Feet)	Symbol on plan and sections (Figs. 20, 21)
Quartz latite porphyry dikes		
Fisher quartz latite	0–100	15
Creede lake beds, water-laid tuff. Miocene	0–2000	13, 14
Erosional interval		
Piedra group: Quartz latite flows and tuff tridymite latite, andesite, rhyolite breccia	300–2150	6–12
Major erosional interval. Deep gorges carved in Alberoto rocks.		
Alberoto group: Equity quartz latite.	0–1000	5
Phoenix Park quartz latite	0–500	4
Intrusive rhyolite		3
Campbell Mountain rhyolite	0–1000	2
Willow Creek rhyolite	0–1000	1

STRUCTURE: The older formations, including those of the Alberoto group (Nos. 1-5) and the two lower formations of the Piedra group (Nos. 6 and 7), have been flexed into an anticline whose axis trends west of north (Figs. 20, 21). The younger rocks in contrast (Nos. 8-15) seem to have undergone little if any folding (Fig. 21, Section A-A').

Three normal faults—the Alpha, Bulldog Mountain, and Amethyst—strike parallel to the anticlinal axis, whereas a fourth, the Solomon Ridge, diverges

63

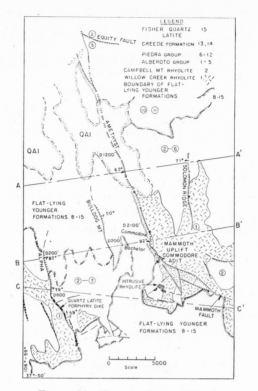

FIGURE 20.—*Structural map of Creede district, Colorado*

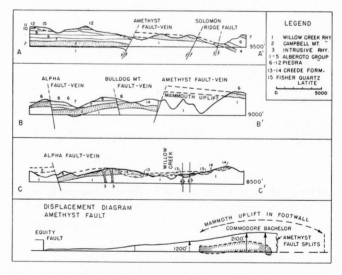

FIGURE 21.—*Sections, Creede district*

slightly and strikes north. Faults west of the axis dip eastward (Alpha, Bulldog Mountain), whereas those east of it dip westward (Amethyst and Solomon Ridge).

Although the Alpha, Bulldog Mountain, and Amethyst faults break the anticline along its crest, the broken crest retains the rise of the arch (Fig. 21, section B-B'). South of Section B-B' the Bulldog Mountain fault disappears, and the Amethyst fault loses its identity in a complex of radiating lesser faults.

In the latitude of Section C-C' the crest of the arch is broken only by the Alpha fault, but it is cut by two longitudinal fissures, filled with rhyolite dikes, with no displacement. The dike fissures cut the rocks of the Alberoto group (Nos. 1 and 2) but seem to end upward at the base of the Piedra group (No. 6), because the rhyolite spread out from the fissures along the eroded surface of the Alberoto rocks.

In the latitude of Section B-B' the eastern flank of the anticline, in the footwall of the Amethyst fault, has been uplifted much more strongly than the western flank, in the footwall of the Alpha fault. The strong uplift on the eastern flank is local and roughly domical. This is shown by the star-shaped outcrop of Willow Creek rhyolite (Fig. 20) which is, with a minor exception, the oldest known formation in the district. The writer has called this irregular dome the Mammoth uplift. The uplift is bounded on the west by the Amethyst fault as far south as the point of splitting on that fault; south of this point the uplift, although extensively faulted, is not bounded by faults.

The Alpha fault also has Willow Creek rhyolite in its footwall opposite the stretch of the Amethyst fault that bounds the Mammoth uplift. On both these faults the throw is at a maximum opposite these structural highs in their footwalls.

Displacement on the Amethyst fault is shown diagrammatically in the Displacement Diagram (Fig. 21). Where the fault bounds the Mammoth uplift the throw on the fault is 2100 feet, but it decreases almost to zero northward, to the point where the Amethyst fault blocks off the eastward-trending Equity fault (Fig. 20); north of this point displacement on the Amethyst instantly increases. Here again displacement on the Amethyst fault is associated with the structural high in its footwall.

On the Alpha fault the throw is 800 feet opposite the structural high in its footwall and decreases quickly northward to where the fault dies out.

Although these faults have been described in relation to an anticline involving only the older formations, they displace both the latter and the flat-lying younger formations.

ANALYSIS OF STRUCTURE: The major faults, which parallel the axis of the anticline, are oriented like tension fissures caused by arching of brittle material (Fig. 1A; Fig. 21, Section A-A', east half; Section B-B'; Section C-C', west half). Most of the original tension fissures are now faults, but rhyolite dikes intruding the older, arched rocks have sealed and preserved two such tension fissures (Section C-C').

The fissures which turned into faults created a compound graben along the crest of the anticline, not dissimilar to the graben on the crest of the Salt Valley anticline in Utah (Fig. 14A).

These facts indicate that the Creede fracture pattern originated during formation of the anticline, and yet these epi-anticlinal faults displace unarched younger strata. It was not a case of the arching dying out toward the surface, because, as shown in Section C-C', flat-lying Creede lake beds (Nos. 13, 14) lie on the eroded crest of the arch. East of Willow Creek, at the same elevation these flat beds match up with similar beds which lie directly on the deeply eroded southern portion of the Mammoth uplift. Hence the arching and the major part of the Mammoth uplift were completed long before Creede time.

The fact that the epi-anticlinal faults displace the flat-lying strata overlying the arch necessitates a second period of uplift, especially on the flanks of the arch (Sections A-A', B-B', C-C'). Renewed uplift of a mosaic of fault blocks would involve no arching but would operate by block faulting. The epi-anticlinal faults were propogated upward through the younger volcanic rocks during this second period of uplift.

Most of the throw on the Amethyst fault at its south end was caused by rise of the irregular Mammoth dome in the fault footwall, just as the half domes at Ophir and Matehuala rose along their bounding faults. (Displacement diagram, Fig. 21). The Mammoth dome rose at about the same time as the major anticline took form, because the fractures upon it were invaded by the same rhyolite (No. 3) that intruded the tension fissures on the anticline, and it is reasonable to assume that intrusion took place while the walls of fissures were being pulled apart by stretching inherent in upfolding. But the dome rose independently of the anticline on which it lies because it shows the radial and concentric fractures typical of doming.

The Amethyst fracture was probably present, but there was no displacement when the Mammoth uplift started; the fracture ended southward in the area of domical uplift. The uplift utilized the Amethyst fracture as a track for upward movement as far as the fracture persisted; where it ended, the uplift jumped westward across the prolongation of the Amethyst fracture.

Displacement on the Alpha fault was also caused by localized rise of its footwall, but uplift here was less centralized and autonomous than in the Mammoth area and probably corresponds to a general rise of the east flank of the anticline.

METALLIZATION: The major veins lie along the major faults. The Amethyst vein furnished the bulk of the production of silver, lead, and zinc. Most of the ore mined was oxidized. Among the primary minerals were argentite, stephanite, galena, and sphalerite, in a gangue of quartz, barite, and fluorite.

The productive area on the Amethyst vein lies at its south end (Fig. 20; Displacement diagram, Fig. 21). Where it carried ore the vein showed crustified banding, drusy cavities, and was in places a quartz-cemented rock breccia.

The veins along the Alpha, Bulldog Mountain, and Solomon Ridge faults differ greatly from the Amethyst. They are mineralized sheeted zones with only minor quartz and lack crustified banding and druses. The Amethyst vein was formed by open-space filling, but these other veins originated by replacement of country rock.

RELATION OF STRUCTURE TO METALLIZATION : Metallization followed the second major period of fault movements; some postmineral faulting took place on all the veins.

The structure of the Amethyst vein in its productive segment strongly suggests pulling apart of its walls during vein formation. The productive segment adjoins on the north the point where the Amethyst fault turns sharply southeastward and loses itself in a series of southeastward trending grabens produced during the doming (Fig. 20). The dome extends southwestward across the prolongation of the normal strike of the Amethyst fault.

Rise of the Mammoth dome was the dominant movement in this area, both in the earlier and in the later periods of deformation. The greater part of the rise was effected in the earlier stage. The footwall of the Amethyst fault rose to its greatest height opposite the apex of the dome, but uplift swept around the end of the fault into the south end of the hanging-wall block and tended to lift that block from the footwall for some distance northward. The southeastward-trending grabens reflect stretching in the northeasterly direction, normal to the strike of the Amethyst fault. In effect, the southern portion of the Amethyst fracture became a radial tension fissure on the Mammoth dome. Hence during this earlier period of uplift the walls of this part of the fault would tend to gape, although relaxation of the uplifting force would allow the hanging wall to settle back in place.

Gaping was resumed after the second period of uplift as the structure of the Amethyst vein shows. This later uplift involved renewed rise of the Mammoth dome; it produced some stretching normal to the main anticline also, because latite porphyry dikes, of relatively late age and probably just preceding metallization, intruded the Amethyst and Alpha fault zones and longitudinal fissures west of the Alpha.

The Amethyst fault was not everywhere utilized as a plane of movement by the second uplift. In the Bachelor area (Fig. 20) the fault strike has a sharp, triangular westward salient; the base of the triangle is a "short-cut" fracture which prolongs the normal course of the fault past the other two legs of the triangle. North and south of the salient the vein follows the Amethyst fault, but at the salient the vein follows the cut-off fissure, along which faulting was minor (Section B-B'.)

The Amethyst vein in its productive segment has many branch veins in its hanging wall. The branches nearly parallel the main vein in strike but dip steeply eastward, toward the westward-dipping main vein (Emmons and Larsen, 1923, Fig. 20, p. 150; Fig. 21, p. 151). These dip branches furnished most of the ore in the last years of mining.

Structurally these branches are feather joints, tension fissures opened by shearing strain brought about by impedence to movement on the main fault. The reason for the impeded movement and consequent disruption of the hanging wall is clear.

The Mammoth dome utilized the Amethyst fault surface to aid its rise, but it reached its greatest height not far north of where the fault disappeared. It was like pushing up a trap door in a ceiling where the door was free to move at one end but nailed fast at the other. The competent Willow Creek rhyolite footwall suffered little in the process, but the less competent Campbell Mountain rhyolite hanging wall was sheared and ruptured by feather joints off the main fault. These tension fissures probably formed during the earlier uplift and were reopened by the later uplift.

The peculiar conditions that favored ore in the south portion of the Amethyst fault were lacking in the veins along the Alpha, Bulldog Mountain, and Solomon Ridge faults. No forces operated to pull their walls apart. Planes of shear, loci for intermittent or continuous fault movements, persisted past the period of metallization. They produced little ore.

SOURCES FOR CREEDE: Larsen (1929); Emmons and Larsen (1923)

ANTELOPE, NEVADA

REGIONAL SETTING: Antelope, a minor silver–gold district in the Great Basin, 30 miles east of Goldfield, lies above a marked structural high in the Precambrian basement (Pl. 1).

ROCK FORMATIONS: Mainly massive Miocene (?) rhyolite flows rest on a basement of quartzite and conglomerate and are intruded by andesite and dacite slightly younger than the rhyolite flows (Fig. 22).

STRUCTURE: The district lies on the east flank of the Cactus range which reflects in its topography the underlying structure, that of a northward-trending anticline with the Antelope district on its eastern flank.

The rhyolite flows at Antelope dip monoclinally eastward and are step-faulted by a series of normal faults striking parallel to the flows but dipping in a direction normal to that of the flows, toward the core of the anticline.

As shown on the cross section, the flows have been intensely sheeted by planes that parallel the step faults. Superimposed on this westward-dipping sheeting is a less extensive vertical sheeting, developed near the faults in their footwall blocks.

Dikes composed of rhyolite similar to that of the flows intrude some of the step faults.

ANALYSIS OF STRUCTURE: The intense sheeting, the planes of which strike parallel to the axis of uplift and dip toward the core of the uplift, probably reflects stretching of the rhyolite flows as they were being axially uplifted. The sheeting resembles the sheeted zones at Sunlight, for which a similar origin was postulated. Formation of tension joints or fissures commonly precedes antithetic block faulting in uplifts of brittle material. At Antelope, as uplift continued the need for antithetic faulting arose, and certain sheeting planes were probably selected as faults.

The vertical sheeting, limited to the immediate footwalls of these antithetic faults, suggests a feather-joint relation to the faults. The hindrance to fault movement which set up the shearing strain to produce the feather joints, may have been caused by flattening of the faults in depth, a fact which Schrader points out. The westward-dipping faults and sheeting originated as tension joints, and therefore they lie normal to the rhyolite beds which they fracture. The underlying

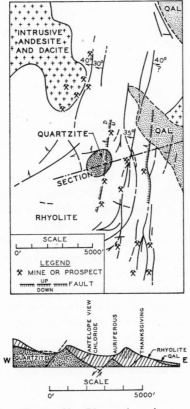

FIGURE 22.—*Plan and section,*
Antelope district, Nevada

quartzite differs physically from the rhyolite, and possibly the faults, on leaving rhyolite to enter quartzite, flattened in dip because of "tectonic refraction".

METALLIZATION: The silver–gold veins carried horn silver and argentite in a gangue of fine-grained replacement quartz, some drusy quartz, adularia, and crushed rhyolite in places altered to clay or sericite.

Most of the veins were along members of the westward-dipping sheeting system and not along the faults except for one, the Auriferous (Fig. 22, Section), but after vein formation many veins underwent minor post-mineral faulting. Average width of the minable veins was 8 feet or less, but there are innumerable quartz stringers throughout the sheeting, too narrow to be mined.

RELATION OF STRUCTURE TO METALLIZATION: Vein formation seems to have taken place during the stage of arching that preceded the block faulting, when flexing and stretching of the rhyolite produced the sheeting and opened the sheeting planes to admit vein matter. After block faulting began, the blocks would topple as units with little or no internal deformation. This probability is strengthened by the fact that nearly all the veins were loci for slight post-mineral fault movements which were probably contemporaneous with the major antithetic fault movements. The fact, also, that the vertical feather-joint sheeting is barren and therefore probably post-mineral fits the notion that antithetic faulting at Antelope was later than the metallization.

SOURCES FOR ANTELOPE: Ball (1907); Schrader (1913)

BODIE, CALIFORNIA

REGIONAL SETTING: The gold–silver camp of Bodie lies within the Great Basin, near its western edge and the eastern scarp of the Sierra Nevada (Pl. 1). The Precambrian crystalline basement probably lies deep here; since Bodie is situated in a re-entrant in the outcrop of the Sierra Nevada batholith, the eastern flank of that massive may underlie Bodie at relatively shallow depth.

ROCK FORMATIONS: The country rock consists of andesitic flows, tuffs, and agglomerate. The lowest exposed rock is hornblende andesite, uniform in appearance and showing little if any suggestion of bedding.

Several hundred feet of andesitic agglomerate and coarse tuff overlie the hornblende andesite. The bedding of the agglomerate series seems to conform to the upper surface of the hornblende andesite (Fig. 24, Sections A-A′, B-B′, C-C′), but the relation of the hornblende andesite to the agglomerate series is not clear. The hornblende andesite may be extrusive in which case the contact with the overlying agglomeratic series is depositional. The hornblende andesite may be intrusive with laccolithic top which has invaded and domed the agglomeratic series. The more likely alternative seems to be that the hornblende andesite consists mainly of massive flows and that its contact with the agglomerate is depositional.

The Bodie Mountain lavas, andesitic flows with intercalated layers of agglomerate, unconformably overlie the agglomerate series in the northwestern part of the district and the hornblende andesite in the eastern and southern parts (Fig. 23). The Bodie Mountain lavas have been stripped by erosion from the central part of the area except for a few remnants capping hornblende andesite at high elevations there.

STRUCTURE: The major structure is that of an irregular anticline trending east of north, upon which are superimposed several domes as shown by the structural contours on the base of the agglomerate series (Fig. 23). The principal dome lies at the north end of the anticline (Bodie Bluff and Standard Hill). Silver Hill, in the central part of the anticline, marks the apex of a second dome.

The cross sections of Figure 24 show that the Bodie Mountain lavas shared in the arching that formed the anticline. The fact that they overlap the older formations southward and rest on the agglomerate series on the northwest and on the hornblende andesite on the southeast suggests deformation antedating the Bodie anticline.

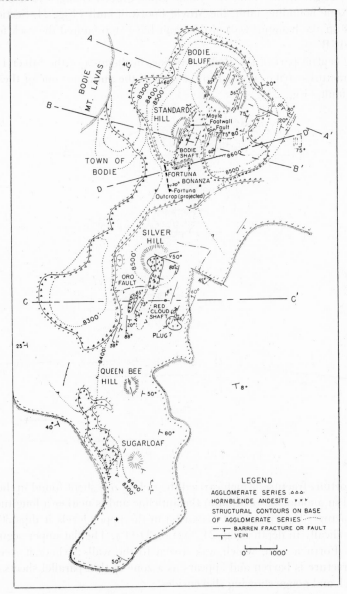

FIGURE 23.—*Structural map of Bodie district, California*

The fracture pattern is typical of an anticlinal upfold. The major faults, fractures, and veins strike parallel to the axis of uplift and dip toward the axial plane (Figs. 23, 24).

On Bodie Bluff a graben block of agglomerate, internally faulted, has been dropped into the underlying hornblende andesite (Fig. 24, Section A-A'). To the south, on Standard Hill, the Bodie Bluff graben changes to a half graben, with only one bounding fault, the Moyle Footwall fault (Fig. 24, Section B-B'). Dip splits off the hanging wall of this fault have step-faulted the rock formations (Section B-B').

In the central part of the Bodie anticline, in the area of the Silver Hill dome, a set of fractures strikes normal to the axis of the anticline; one of these may be a sizable fault (Fig. 23).

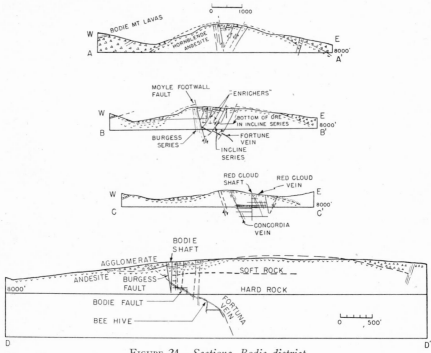

FIGURE 24.—*Sections, Bodie district*

The Fortuna fracture, which carried the richest ore shoot found in the district, is oriented in anomolous relation to the anticline and is neither a longitudinal nor a cross fracture. It strikes west of north; in the upper levels it dips 30° E. but steepens radically in depth (Fig. 24, Section D-D'). The flat upper segment contained the Fortuna vein, which was frozen to the walls; where it steepens the Fortuna fracture is barren and appears as a zone of thin parallel sheets of highly altered rock and gouge showing slickensides.

ANALYSIS OF STRUCTURE: The Fortuna is the earliest known fracture, because it is cut or displaced by fractures of every other set that meets it. Its anomalous attitude suggests an origin alien to that of the other sets, which fit into the pattern typical of anticlinal upfolds.

The fact that the Bodie Mountain lavas rest on the agglomerate series in the northwest part of the district, but overlie hornblende andesite elsewhere suggests that an uplift existed, perhaps east of the Bodie anticline, before extrusion of the Bodie Mountain lavas, and that the agglomerate had been stripped from this highland before the Bodie Mountain extrusion. If so, the Fortuna fracture could have been originally a tension joint dipping eastward, toward the axis of the older uplift. The role played by the Fortuna in the development of the Bodie anticline will be described.

Arching of the volcanic rocks to form the Bodie anticline produced longitudinal sheeting, arranged in fan pattern in cross section, much like that at Antelope. Irelan (1888) states that the numerous veins in the far northern Bodie Bluff area dip steeply eastward, west of a northward-trending plane, and steeply westward, east of that plane. Section A-A' of Figure 24 shows the pattern but only a few of the sheeting planes. In this area, as at Antelope, certain sheeting planes were selected as loci for faults which produced the compound graben there.

Farther south, in the Standard Hill area, antithetic faulting in the hanging wall of the Moyle Footwall fault has disturbed the picture, but longitudinal tension joints appear in the footwall of the fault (Burgess series) (Fig. 24, section C-C')

In the Bodie shaft area, south of Standard Hill, arching is less pronounced than on the north; here the tension fissures dip nearly vertically (Fig. 24, Section D-D'). This follows from the mechanics of rupture caused by bending.

The fan pattern of tension fissures persists at least as far south as the Silver Hill or Red Cloud area (Fig. 24, Section C-C').

Faulting succeeded jointing and fissuring at Bodie, as at Antelope. The tectonic history can be traced best by considering the effects of anticlinal arching on the pre-existing Fortuna fracture.

The effect of arching on a pre-existing fracture oriented like the Fortuna but with initially steeper dips in its two segments is shown in Figure 25 (upper sketch). The lower, steeper segment would remain almost unchanged in dip, but the upper, flatter segment would flatten.

A rising and expanding arch with a pre-existing fracture in its flank like the lower segment of the Fortuna might utilize it as a reverse fault aiding the uplift (Fig. 25). Apparently it did, because the lower segment shows gouge and slickensides; in the upper segment, however, the vein was frozen to solid walls. As shown in Figure 25, lower sketches, reverse movement on the steeper segment would create an opening along the flatter segment; as the upper segment flattened, the gaping would widen, provided the rock was strong enough to sustain the roof. The Fortuna stopes stood open for many years after the ore was removed, and they may be still open.

The flat segment of the Fortuna would continue to open as long as the core of the arch rose as a unit, but opening would cease if arching were carried to the point where the core was broken into fault blocks which by antithetic rotation moved downward and opposed rise of the arch. Sections A-A' and B-B' of Figure 24 show that this occurred in the northern portion of the arch.

The Fortuna bonanza lay south of this highly faulted area (Fig. 23 and Section D-D' of Fig. 24). Here conditions favored opening of the Fortuna fracture by the mechanism described, because the rising arch was not broken into fault blocks. The Fortuna vein terminated on the north just within the highly faulted area; the fracture, a feature antedating the arching, may persist northward, but if so it was not opened to receive vein matter.

The Moyle Footwall fault, dipping eastward, originated as a tension fissure; on the east side of the fault numerous westward-dipping tension fissures served as antithetic faults (Fig. 24, Section B-B'). These faults, on approaching the Moyle Footwall fault, bend suddenly upward (Fig. 26, right-hand sketch).

A well-known clay experiment, first performed by H. Cloos, supplies a clue to this behavior. A clay cake was pulled laterally each way from a central axis. A graben aligned along the axis dropped as the clay mass on each side withdrew

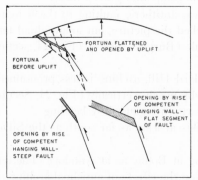

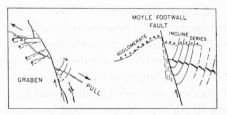

FIGURE 25.—Effect of arching on a   FIGURE 26.—Part of Bodie fracture system
       pre-existing fracture   compared to clay experiment

slightly. (This experiment is illustrated by Bucher, 1933, Fig. 33, p. 145, and Fig. 86, p. 338; by Wisser, 1937, Fig. 11, p. 467; and by Hills, 1941, Fig. 41, p. 65.)

A graben formed on the crest of a rising and expanding arch originates in the same manner, except that the stretching is produced by upbending, and the abutments of the graben rise with respect to sea level whereas the graben block lags behind.

Figure 26 compares a cross section through the Standard mine at Bodie with a cross section of the graben experiment, turned upside down for comparison. Gravity caused the graben block to tend to move along the fault, but the sharp jog in the fault surface (near top of diagram) impeded movement and set up a shearing strain in both walls of the fault. The clay of the graben block flowed in the strained zone bordering the fault; the flow was effected by rotation of thin septa separated by slip surfaces, a few of which are shown.

The clay in the other wall of the fault did not tend to move along the fault but was pulled away from it. Tension fissures formed normal to the direction of pull; where they lay within the strained zone bordering the fault they served as slip surfaces to effect flow. The septa between the slip surfaces were rotated sufficiently to displace antithetically the layer in the clay shown.

In the Standard mine, tension joints east of the Moyle Footwall fault lie normal to the direction of stretching induced by arching, and dip westward, toward the fault, because they are east of the crest.

As shown in Figure 24, Section B-B', and in Figure 26, the uplift here was asymmetric and was concentrated in the footwall of the Moyle Footwall fault, whereas the half graben on the east side of the fault lagged.

After formation of the Moyle Footwall fracture, and probably before faulting on it began, the adjacent rock was softened by hydrothermal alteration. When the footwall started to rise to produce faulting, impedance to the movement set up strong shearing strain in the hanging wall. The impedance was probably caused by irregularities in the fault surface, not shown in Section B-B' of Figure 24, which is partly diagrammatic.

Where the westward-dipping tension joints approached the fault they entered the softened zone where the shearing strain was relieved by flow which strongly dragged the tension joints. The shearing strain extended outward from the fault beyond the softened layer, and into competent rock where strain was relieved not by flow but by antithetic rotation of nearly rigid fault blocks.

ROCK ALTERATION: The hornblende andesite and the agglomerate have been extensively altered. Along the lower flanks of the anticline the rock is mildly propylitized, and this type of alteration grows stronger toward the crest. On the crest, in a belt from Standard Hill to Silver Hill (Fig. 23), the rock is bleached almost white, probably through a combination of sericitization and hydrothermal kaolinization. In the Standard Hill area this bleaching and softening persisted downward to about the tops of the ore shoots, at which level the rock becomes hard and shows little visible alteration (Fig. 24, Section D-D').

METALLIZATION: Important ore deposits were confined to the hornblende andesite in the axial portion of the Bodie anticline. Most of the longitudinal fractures in the Bodie Bluff-Standard Hill area, which form a fan pattern in Sections A-A' and B-B', (Fig. 24), are veins. In the Bodie Bluff area the veins were more closely spaced but narrower than to the south; resemblance to the Antelope mineralized sheeting is close. Ore here was shallow, and production minor.

The bulk of the gold–silver production came from the Standard Hill area, from the Standard mine on the north and the Bodie mine on the south. The westward-dipping antithetic faults of Section B-B' carried veins (called the "Incline" series). The narrower veins of the Burgess series, in the footwall of the Moyle Footwall fault, yielded limited but rich gold ore. South of Section B-B', in the Bodie mine, the flat-dipping segment of the Fortune fracture yielded the largest and richest ore shoot (Section D-D').

Veins of the westward-dipping or Incline series were formed in part by replacement of thinly sheeted rock, but mainly by filling of openings; most contained banded quartz, separated sharply from the vein walls, which were well defined. Some veins showed breccia structure of rock fragments cemented by vein matter. In the veins which displace the Fortuna vein (Section B-B') the quartz itself was often crushed to sugar.

The westward-dipping veins seldom exceeded 20 inches in width, but one, the Standard, averaged 20 feet in width.

Silver occurred as cerargyrite in the upper oxidized portions of the westward-dipping veins and as argentite and native silver below. Pyrite was moderately abundant, but sphalerite and galena seem to have been lacking.

Ore shoots on veins of the Incline series pitched southward and bottomed about 500 feet below the surface. Veins that were productive above this horizon showed, below it, only sheeted zones mineralized with barren quartz, or merely barren belts of thinly sheeted rock. The productive veins weakened upward also; they ramified on entering the layer of bleached and softened rock and ended at the contact of hornblende andesite with the overlying agglomerate series.

The rich but narrow Burgess veins in the footwall of the Moyle Footwall fault (Section B-B') carried quartz with crustified banding.

The Fortuna bonanza, shown on the plan (Fig. 23), averaged 200 feet in strike length but extended down dip for 1000 feet. Throughout the ore shoot the vein dipped 30° E., but below the bottom of ore the fracture steepened to 45° or more. The Fortuna bonanza near its bottom left the Fortuna fracture for the vertical Beehive minor fracture in the footwall (Fig. 24, Section D-D'). Ore on the Beehive terminated 175 feet below the Fortuna, and the vein split into seams of barren quartz.

The average width of ore in the Fortuna segment was 2 feet or less. The quartz was unbroken, hard, and tightly frozen to the walls. In many places it showed drusy cavities and comb structure. Metallic minerals included native gold and silver, argentite, pyrite, and sphalerite; with depth sphalerite increased as gold diminished.

RELATION OF STRUCTURE TO METALLIZATION: All Bodie veins carried both silver and gold, but some were relatively high in silver, some in gold. Where earlier vein matter was fractured and later vein minerals deposited in the openings created, the later vein matter was invariably richer in gold than the earlier. Solutions therefore changed in time from relatively silver-rich to relatively gold-rich. On this basis, it is possible to postulate the relative ages of vein systems (but not necessarily of fracture systems). From oldest to youngest, the vein systems seem to rank as follows:

(1) Fortuna bonanza; silver relatively high

(2) Westward-dipping or Incline series; much higher in gold than the Fortuna

(3) Burgess system, in the footwall of the Moyle Footwall fault, and a steeply dipping set of veinlets in the hanging-wall block which cut the westward-dipping Incline series veins and enriched them; miners called them the enrichers (Section B-B'). The Burgess veins and the enrichers were fabulously high in gold.

Longitudinal tension fissures form at an early stage of arching, but a fracture already there, like the Fortuna, would perhaps be affected by arching at an equally early stage. Rise of its hanging-wall block as an unbroken unit would cause the flat segment of the Fortuna fracture to gape and permit entry of vein-forming solutions. At the same time steeply dipping tension joints might form. Many members of the westward-dipping sheeting system cross the Fortuna vein with little or no displacement, and in general these "crossings" coincided with enrichment of the Fortuna ore, indicating that the tension joints were there when the ore formed. After vein formation, many of these joints became step faults which displaced the Fortuna ore body and are clearly post mineral (Fig. 24, Section D-D').

Veins of the westward-dipping Incline series north of the Fortuna bonanza (Fig. 24, Section B-B') may have formed at about the time that continued arching started to turn tension fissures into antithetic faults. Whereas many veins of the system were frozen to their walls, others lay along the antithetic faults and had clay selvages containing ore-bearing quartz fragments along their walls. While much of this faulting was postmineral, some was probably intramineral, because older vein material was fractured and younger vein minerals were deposited in the openings thus created.

The gold-rich Burgess veins (Section B-B') with their banded and drusy quartz frozen to the walls and the similar "enrichers" in the half graben east of the Moyle Footwall fault occupied typical tension joints which seem to be of relatively late origin and to have formed by renewed arching and stretching during the final stages of metallization. Such stretching in the unbroken footwall block of the Moyle Footwall fault is less surprising than the possibility of renewed arching and stretching in the broken hanging-wall block. This may have been possible because the fault blocks here had rotated as far as they could and had become locked.

SOURCES FOR BODIE: Brown (1907); Francis Frederick (1940), field maps, unpublished reports, and personal communication; Irelan (1888); McLaughlin (1907)

GUANAJUATO, GUANAJUATO, MEXICO

REGIONAL SETTING: The great silver camp of Guanajuato lies in south-central Mexico (Pl. 1). The region is covered mainly by Tertiary extrusive rocks that form the southeast end of the great volcanic province of the Sierra Madre Occidental; but the basement on which the volcanic rocks rest is exposed at Guanajuato, where it consists of Triassic (?) metasediments.

The axis of the Occidental geanticline, a positive and intermittently rising element from the Upper Jurassic through the Cretaceous, passes through Guanajuato. The crystalline basement may lie deep here, but not so deep as to the east, where the Mexican geosyncline sagged while the geanticline rose in Late Jurassic and Cretaceous times.

ROCK FORMATIONS:

Age	Formation	Thickness (Feet)
Tertiary	Intrusive monzonite and monzonite porphyry Granite batholith Upper rhyolite flow Intrusive andesite Andesite tuffs, breccias, and flows Lower rhyolite flows and breccias Guanajuato conglomerate; conglomerate with shale and sandstone horizon	400 Top eroded 1300 maximum 0–1300 2000 maximum
Triassic (?)	La Luz basalts (nw part of district) La Luz schist; schists derived from rhyolite; slate derived from shale; layers of marble and quartzite	1000 ?

STRUCTURE: The district lies on the northeast flank of a major anticline which plunges southeastward. The northeast flank carries three major faults which parallel the anticlinal axis and dip toward it (Fig. 27, after Wandke and Mar-

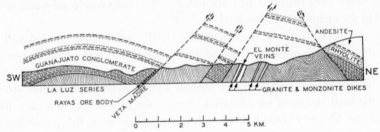

FIGURE 27.—Cross section, Guanajuato district, Mexico

tínez, 1928). Two of these faults are normal, the third is reverse. Dikes of granite and monzonite parallel these westward-dipping faults. An eastward-dipping northward-striking fault with large normal throw bounds the district on the east.

The crest of the arch passes through the western portion of the district. The most westerly vein fractures, in the northwest part of the district, northwest of the section of Figure 27, dip for the most part northeastward and lie on the southwest flank of the arch near its crest.

The faulting has greatly dislocated the arch. Either the northeast flank has been abnormally uplifted with respect to the rest of the arch, or the crest abnormally depressed. The relatively high northeast flank has a dropped block within it.

The crest of the anticline carries a half graben or possibly a normal graben (the southwest flank is but little exposed). The visible graben fault, on the northeast flank, is the Veta Madre, with a throw in the area of the section of about 1000 m. The fault has been traced for 25 km. Over most of its course it is slightly sinuous in plan but without sharp jogs; but several km southeast of the section of Figure 25 the Veta Madre fault joins an eastward-striking southward-dipping fracture, and the fault movement follows this fracture east for 1 km at which point the faulting deserts the eastward-trending fracture and resumes the normal southeasterly course.

Faulting on the Veta Madre decreases southeastward; at the eastward-striking segment the throw is 800 m; 7 km to the southeast fracture and displacement disappear.

The granite batholith invaded the anticline in the northwest part of the district in the highest part of the plunging fold; it occupies not only the crestal portion but also part of the northeast flank of the fold. The Veta Madre toward its northwest end enters the batholith and persists within it for 5 km.

ANALYSIS OF STRUCTURE: Upfolding of the strata to form the Guanajuato anticline and the formation of longitudinal tension fissures began before intrusion of the batholith because dikes of andesite, antedating the granite intrusion, parallel the axis of the anticline and invaded tension fissures created by the arching. Upward warping of the anticlinal axis, which gives it its southeastward plunge, had also commenced before the batholithic intrusion because early andesite dikes fill northeast cross fractures where the fold plunges southeastward. Some of these cross dikes are convex to the southeast in plan and resemble the arcuate cross joints on the plunging noses of the anticline of Figure 1F.

Upfolding, but as yet no faulting, continued during intrusion of the batholith. Wandke and Martínez believe the intrusion was forcible and accounts for part of the anticlinal uplift (1928, p. 14).

Uplift and fissuring continued after solidification of the pluton, because a northeast-striking granite porphyry dike, oriented as a cross joint, intruded the batholith, and granite dikes occupy longitudinal tension fissures cutting across a roof pendant in the batholith. Similar dikes fill longitudinal tension fissures in La Luz slates on the northeast flank of the anticline (Fig. 27). The Veta Madre fault itself probably originated as a great tension fissure because before faulting the fracture was invaded in places by dikes of granite porphyry.

Next came the breakup of the arch (Fig. 27). The Guanajuato anticline, like the Creede anticline, was broken during upfolding by major tension fissures; in both districts differential movement of the resulting blocks dominated the closing stages of deformation. One such block, well down the northeast flank of the Guanajuato anticline, seems to have risen, with respect to sea level (El Monte horst, Fig. 27). Between this block and the crest, the dropped sliver block and what appears to be rotational flattening of the Veta Madre fault suggest strong lateral stretching in a direction normal to the axis of the anticline.

Wandke and Martínez point out the relation between the northwest rise of the anticlinal axis and displacement on the Veta Madre fault, stating that the fault ". . . begins almost at the southeast nose of the fold and continues as a rotational fault well into the fold; the amount of faulting increases to the northwest" (1928, p. 15).

Thus the Veta Madre faulting is genetically related to the upfolding; whereas it was in itself a surface of shear, the normal faulting on it which produced the half graben on the crest of the anticline was a result of lateral stretching of an arching plate. The stretching was so strong that the block in the footwall of the Veta Madre rotated somewhat down the flank of the arch. The average dip of the Veta Madre, 42°, is considerably less than that of most graben faults.

When the block faulting was completed, the blocks seem to have become "locked" and unable to move differentially further like the antithetic fault blocks of the Incline series at Bodie. There is evidence for resumption of arching at the time of metallization at Guanajuato, as at Bodie.

METALLIZATION: The Guanajuato silver veins, of epithermal type, formed after the block faulting and probably after erosion had considerably lowered the surface of the uplift because epithermal ore bodies in a given district tend to form at a more or less fixed distance below the surface at the time of mineralization. At Pachuca the distance between that surface and the tops of the ore bodies was about 900-1000 m (Wisser, 1951, p. 472, Fig. 4). The Guanajuato ore bodies occupy a fairly consistent ore zone. Figure 27 shows that if the tops of these ore bodies lay, as at Pachuca, about 1000 m below the surface at the time of mineralization, more than 1000 m must have been eroded from the higher portions of the range.

The Guanajuato silver district contains three mineral belts, each trending northwestward with the axis of the anticline and the strike of the major faults.

(1) The La Luz belt in the northwest part of the district and on the southwest limb of the anticline. The country rock consists of granite of the batholith and a northwestward-trending roof pendant of metabasalt enclosed in granite. The veins, which strike northwestward, lie in the batholith and along the northeast and southwest borders of the roof pendant. All veins but one dip northeastward toward the axis of the anticline.

(2) The Guanajuato belt proper, in the center, the most productive vein of which is the Veta Madre, dipping southwestward toward the axis of the anticline (Fig. 27).

(3) The Santa Rosa–El Monte–Peregrina belt on the northeast, the veins of which dip southwestward, toward the axis of the anticline (Fig. 27).

The ore bodies carry silver and gold; the gold–silver ratio is 1:100. The principal gangue minerals are quartz and calcite. The quartz is fine-grained, drusy, with colloform banding. Adularia, dolomite, siderite, and ankerite are present. Pyrite is the most abundant sulfide; chalcopyrite, bornite, sphalerite, and galena occur sparingly. The chief silver mineral is argentite, but nearly the whole ruby-silver suite is present as well. All ore minerals are extremely fine-grained.

Quartz was deposited in four surges, one at the start of the period of vein formation, two in the middle, and one at the end. Calcite is younger than the earliest quartz, but the bulk of the calcite was deposited before the mid-point of quartz deposition. Ore minerals were relatively late; they fill fractures in quartz, replace quartz, or are associated with a special type of quartz cutting older, barren quartz.

Structurally the ore bodies fall into two classes: (1) tabular bodies, either simple filled fissures or fissure-replacement bodies; (2) stockworks.

Narrow veins, and the narrower segments of wider veins, are likely to be simple filled fissures with well-defined walls. Wider portions of the major veins seem to have formed by replacement of rock fragments combined with open-space deposition in interstices of the rock rubble.

Stockworks consist of mineralized irregularly shattered ground forming a complex of intersecting quartz-calcite stringers often rich in silver; the rock between is barren, and the over-all silver content of the ore bodies is low. Three stockwork ore bodies were mined, all in the immediate hanging wall of the Veta Madre.

The Veta Madre carried four great tabular ore bodies within a stretch of 4 km. The ore shoots lay along a well-defined axis plunging gently northwestward and were slightly elongated parallel to this axis. At least three of the ore bodies centered at cups or depressions in the Veta Madre footwall.

Over most of the productive stretch on the Veta Madre, Guanajuato conglomerate forms the hanging wall, La Luz schist the footwall. The Valenciana ore body, at the northwest end of the stretch, formed where both walls are schist.

Whereas the tabular ore bodies on the Veta Madre occurred mainly at cups or concavities in the footwall, the stockworks, which extended as much as 100 m out into the hanging wall block, were localized opposite humps in the Veta Madre footwall. The Veta Madre itself was barren in these hump areas. (Wandke and Martínez, 1928, p. 23-25, Figs. 4, 5).

RELATION OF STRUCTURE TO METALLIZATION: Although metallization at Guanajuato took place not only after completion of the major faulting but also after considerable erosion of the faulted blocks, several features suggest resumption of arching of the anticline at the time of metallization.

(1) The major veins of La Luz, on the southwest flank of the anticline, near the crest, and minor veins on the northeast flank, such as those of El Monte (Fig. 27), show crustified banding and druses suggesting that the fissure walls were pulling apart during vein formation.

(2) The crest of the arch is not broken by major faults and preserves the rise of the arch (Fig. 27).

(3) Fault movements, although slight, were resumed on the Veta Madre at the time of vein formation because barren parts of the vein are made up of early quartz and calcite whereas ore solutions penetrated cracks in the early gangue and were deposited around fragments.

The Veta Madre fracture, before the major premineral faulting on it, was not everywhere planar but was in places slightly warped into "cups," concave toward the hanging wall, and "humps," convex toward the hanging wall. Most of the major ore bodies on the Veta Madre were localized where faulting moved a broad, shallow cup in the footwall surface opposite a planar area of the hanging-wall surface. Ore formed by replacement of rock fragments fallen into the opening thus created and filling of interstices between the boulders. Inspection of pillars and breasts in the great open stopes of the Cata, Rayas, and Valenciana mines convinced this writer that much of the rubble fell from the hanging wall during formation of the vein, and that the fall of boulders finally choked the opening and supported the back, and thus interstices were preserved between the boulders, to be filled by vein matter. Renewed fault movement best explains this intramineral renewal of spalling.

The stockworks in the hanging wall of the Veta Madre were created where a hump in the footwall surface was brought opposite a planar portion of the hanging-wall surface. Wandke and Martínez attribute the stockwork to shattering of the hanging-wall block as it moved over the hump (1928, p. 24).

In 1928 Wandke showed the writer the stockwork being mined in the Sirena mine, at the southeast end of the ore stretch on the Veta Madre. The veinlets showed crustified banding and were clearly formed by open-space filling of the stockwork fractures. Evidence was so plain that the fractures were opening as vein matter filled them that Wandke and Martínez concluded that the fracture walls were forced apart mainly by pressure of ore solutions (1928, p. 25). The writer believes that the stockwork fractures, which may have formed during the major premineral fault movements, were opened, or reopened, by renewed but hindered movement on the Veta Madre fault. The renewed movement can best be explained by renewed uplift.

The northwest end of the Veta Madre lies within the batholith and is barren there. With one reversal, ore bodies on the Veta Madre decrease in importance southeastward away from the batholith. The greatest ore body, that of the Valenciana, lies nearest the batholith, and the smallest, that of the Sirena, lies farthest away. At Guanajuato, as in many districts containing major intrusive masses, the suggestion is strong that the trunk channel for ore-bearing solutions was the periphery of the intrusion, in this case the southern edge of the batholith. The Valenciana ore body may owe its size to proximity to the trunk channel. The only productive veins within the batholith are those of La Luz, and they lie along the northeast and southeast contacts of the metabasalt roof pendant. Ore-forming solutions probably utilized the walls of the roof pendant as channels for ascent.

SOURCES FOR GUANAJUATO: Wandke and Martínez (1928); Wisser (1928), unpublished report and field notes

EL ORO, MEXICO AND MICHOACAN, MEXICO

REGIONAL SETTING: The El Oro gold–silver district is situated 100 km southeast of Guanajuato. The crest line of the Late Cretaceous geanticline probably passed through this area (Pl. 1). It is remarkable how the many Tertiary anticlines associated with ore districts in Mexico parallel in their trend the structural gain established in Cretaceous and earlier time by the Occidental geanticline and its complementary Mexican trough.

ROCK FORMATIONS: No measured stratigraphic section is available. It is convenient to divide the formations into those antedating and those succeeding the period of metallization.

PREMINERAL ROCKS: The oldest exposed formation consists of dark fissile shale with limy zones. The shales occur as an isolated window in a great field of Tertiary and younger volcanic rocks. In the western part of the district massive limestone resembling Middle Cretaceous limestone of known sections rests on the shale, apparently with angular unconformity (Fig. 28).

Unconformably overlying the shale series are remnants of a series of flows, locally called the Augite Andesite formation. Similar rock intrudes shale as a flat sheet 600 feet thick, in the area of the San Rafael vein (Figs. 28-31). This sheet

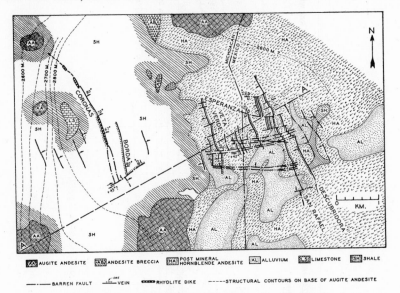

FIGURE 28.—*Structural map of El Oro district, Mexico*

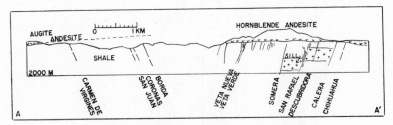

FIGURE 29.—*General section of El Oro district*

is quartz diorite according to Foshag (1942, unpublished compilation on El Oro).

Quartz porphyry dikes intrude the shale series and follow the northwesterly trend of the major veins. The Coronas vein lies in the hanging wall of such a dike (Fig. 28), and a quartz porphyry dike accompanies in places the Veta Verde.

POSTMINERAL ROCKS: After intrusion of the dikes and after vein formation a rolling surface was produced by erosion. Upon this surface were poured out extensive flows of hornblende andesite, which cap many ore bodies. These extru-

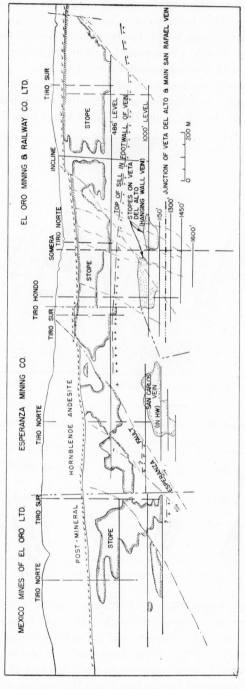

FIGURE 30.—*Vertical longitudinal projection, San Rafael vein*

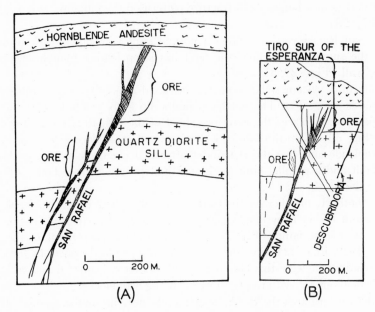

FIGURE 31.—*Cross sections, San Rafael lode*

sives cover most of the eastern part of the district but are lacking in the western part (Fig. 28).

STRUCTURE: Deformation took place in two widely separated periods. The earlier deformation is reflected in the structure of the shale. In the western area the beds are folded into gentle anticlines and synclines. Less is known of the structure in the eastern area, where hornblende andesite overlies the shale which crops out only in the small window shown in Figure 27. Here the shale beds stand almost vertically. Shale is extensively exposed in mine workings west of the window, but data on its structure are scanty. Lindgren (1913, unpublished report) speaking of the area of the San Rafael vein, says that the shale there is flat lying and calls the flat quartz diorite sheet there a sill (Fig. 29).

The second deformation is reflected chiefly in the fracture pattern and in the attitudes of the remnants of the augite andesite flow series. The fracture pattern suggests a broad anticline because the major fractures form a parallel system, the members of which strike north-northwestward, the western fractures dipping eastward, and the eastern fractures westward (Figs. 28, 29).

The scattered remnants of augite andesite flows strengthen this suggestion. Elevations of the shale–augite andesite contact, taken from the geologic map of Flores (1920, Pl. 2), permit the drawing of sketchy structural contours on the base of the flows (Fig. 28). The contours suggest that the flows were upfolded as a fat anticline or elongate dome trending north-northwestward parallel to the strike of the major fractures, and that the anticline plunges north-northwestward. To the north the Coronas and Borda vein fractures swing toward the west and suggest flaring of a longitudinal fracture pattern on the plunging nose of an anticline (Fig. 28).

The San Rafael vein lies along a normal fault with downthrow toward the axis of the supposed anticline; the fault has steep feather-joint branches in its hanging wall (Figs. 29, 31).

Faults of a system striking nearly eastward cross the vein fractures in the eastern area (Fig. 28). The northerly faults dip flatly north. One of the group, the Esperanza, displaces the main ore shoot of the San Rafael vein down to the north (Fig. 30). Two-thirds of the displacement took place before extrusion of the hornblende andesite, the remainder after that event. A branch of the Esperanza fault and a parallel fault to the north step fault the ore body still farther down to the north.

The southerly members of the transverse fault system dip more steeply northward (about 65°). They displace the Veta Verde and San Rafael veins in the manner of reverse faults (Fig. 28), but longitudinal projections of these veins (Flores, 1920, Pl. 6, 12) show the ore shoots dropped to the north by these faults. These relations indicate that the footwall blocks moved upward and eastward at an angle of about 45° with respect to the hanging wall blocks.

In the western area the Borda vein fracture near its southern end is displaced by a northeast fault dipping steeply northward. The direction of heave suggests reverse faulting (Fig. 28), but Flores states (1920, p. 61) that this fault, like all others of the district, is a normal fault. Here again relations demand movement of the footwall obliquely upward, in this case at 45° up and to the west.

ANALYSIS OF STRUCTURE: Although the eastward-trending fractures in the eastern area are now mainly postmineral faults, this fracture system may have been among the earliest to form. The Esperanza fault, belonging to this system, is paralleled in strike and dip by a nearby quartz diorite dike, representing the earliest intrusive rock type. The San Rafael vein fault displaces this dike, and, although the Esperanza fault displaced the San Rafael vein fault in postmineral time, the suggestion is that this fault movement took place on a fracture belonging to a system which had long existed.

The eastward-trending fractures bear no apparent relation to the El Oro anticline. Their mode of origin is not clear, but it seems likely that they antedated the north-northwestward-trending fractures.

The earliest fracturing produced by upfolding of the anticline seems to have taken the form of longitudinal tension fissures, which were promptly invaded by quartz porphyry dikes.

Graben faulting along the north-northwestward-trending vein fractures came next. The faulting antedated the mineralization and resulted presumably from continued uplift. Early vein matter sealed the faults in places and prevented further fault movements, but the urge for such movements remained strong. The resulting shearing strain produced the many feather joints in the walls of these sealed faults.

Further analysis of El Oro structure is so closely linked with the processes of vein formation that it must be postponed until the mineralization has been described.

METALLIZATION : All known ore deposits occurred in veins along north-north-westward-trending fractures (ore stretches are shown by dots in Figure 28). The productive zone trends eastward, transverse to the strike of the veins.

Ore deposits fall into two classes which differ in composition and age.

EARLIER ORE : This comprises relatively low-grade gold-quartz veins with sparse sulfides and is exemplified by the largest veins, the San Rafael and Veta Verde. The gold-bearing quartz formed partly by replacing barren coarsely crystalline calcite, partly by open-space filling.

Oxidation of these veins antedated extrusion of the hornblende andesite and made mining possible through residual enrichment of gold by leaching of barren calcite intergrown with the quartz. In spite of enrichment, gold content averaged only about 0.4 ounce per ton. The gold–silver ratio ranged from 1 :6 to 1 :14.

Beneath the ore shoots the gold content dropped rapidly until it reached zero, at a horizon where the veins narrow and carry only fine-grained quartz formed mainly by replacement of the fracture walls. The dropoff in gold at this horizon suggests that the primary gold bottomed at essentially the same horizon as did the enriched ore.

The San Rafael and Veta Verde veins widen remarkably upward from where they pinch. The wider portions consisted chiefly of shattered, silicified shale cemented by vein matter. The San Rafael vein was not minable over the entire width of these wider segments. Relatively small ore shoots lay along the footwall or near the center of the vein in the Esperanza section (Fig. 30).

The San Rafael fault displaced the thick quartz diorite sill before the San Rafael vein formed along the fault (Figs. 29, 31). The top of the sill in the footwall of the fault is shown on the longitudinal projection (Fig. 30) and on the cross sections (Fig. 31). Ore on the San Rafael vein proper bottomed at or near the top of the sill in the footwall.

The cross sections show that feather-joint branches in the hanging wall of the San Rafael fault vein are most abundant where the fault displaces the sill. Those leaving the fault near the top of the footwall segment of the sill carried ore of the earlier type, like that of the main vein; and indeed they were so numerous that they contributed to the width of the main vein where they left it, by spread of mineralization within the acute angle between the feather joints and the parent fracture.

An entirely distinct group of feather joints leaves the main San Rafael fault vein at levels far below the bottom of the low-grade, earlier type of gold ore (Fig. 31). Ore on these splits seems to be intermediate in type between the earlier low-grade gold ore and ore of the later type.

The Veta Verde vein is smaller than the San Rafael, is weaker structurally, branches in dip and strike, and nearly disappears in places. It lies entirely in shale because the quartz diorite sill pinches out to the west, between the San Rafael vein and the Veta Verde (Fig. 28). The San Rafael vein fracture extended for considerable distances north and south past its ore stretch, but the Veta Verde fracture disappeared not far north and south of where it carried ore (Fig. 28). Otherwise the two veins are quite similar, for the Veta Verde also carried ore-bearing feather joints in its hanging wall, and it too abruptly pinched and became barren in depth.

LATER ORE: The later ore surge was relatively rich in silver, and the gangue, although it contained some quartz, was dominantly calcite. The silver occurred as argentite, stephanite, and pyrargyrite. The Borda vein, among the eastward-dipping veins of the western area, carried ore of this type, as did several west-ward-dipping veins in the eastern area between the San Rafael vein and the Veta Nueva.

Flores (1920, p. 76) considers the silver-bearing veins younger than the gold veins because stringers of silver ore cut gold veins and cut also, without displacement, minor faults which dislocate gold veins.

A vein type intermediate between that of the gold veins and that of the silver veins is exemplified by the feather joints which leave the San Rafael fault-vein hanging wall at horizons well below the bottom of the gold ore on that vein (Fig. 31). The ore in these veins contained both gold and silver, but the proportion of silver was far higher than that in the main vein, and the ore was much richer, even in gold. According to Lindgren (1913, unpublished report) where the main lode carried 0.4 ounce of gold and 2 ounces of silver per ton, feather-joint branches yielded ore containing 1.5 ounces gold and 15 ounces silver.

The top of ore on these silver-rich feather joints was far below the bottom of ore on the main vein (Figs. 30, 31).

RELATION OF STRUCTURE TO METALLIZATION: Vein formation took place after the faulting on the San Rafael and parallel fractures. When stretching of a crustal plate by upfolding produces faults, faulting seldom stops as long as uplift continues unless the fault blocks rotate and become locked, as at Bodie and Guanajuato. No rotation is evident on the El Oro fault blocks, but faulting ceased while uplift continued. Cessation of faulting seems to have been partly due to sealing of the faults by early vein matter. The faults lie for the most part in shale which was intensively shattered along the faults. Early mineralizing solutions silicified the shale fragments and cemented them with quartz. The resulting tabular zone along the faults was decidedly stronger than the shale adjoining it; further faulting was prevented along the sealed faults, and deformation during the mild up-folding was not strong enough to rip open the shale next to the faults and produce new faults.

The sealing of the faults took place mainly at lower horizons and was not continuous even there. Above, where the walls of the faults were not welded to-gether, they tended to gape apart, or rather the rock adjoining them tended to shatter loosely; simple master fissures seldom form in shale.

Gaping or brecciation took place because the vein fractures were again longi-tudinal tension fissures on the flanks of an anticline that continued to rise and expand. The rise and expansion continued even after mineralization, as is shown by the movement of the footwall blocks of certain eastward-trending faults. It has been pointed out that on the east flank of the arch these blocks moved up and to the east; on the west flank, up and to the west. Such movements, radial with respect to the axis of the arch, recall movements of the material involved in the doming at Ophir which were radial with respect to the center of doming (Fig. 6).

The zone of eastward-trending faults is essentially coextensive with the ore-bearing zone in the eastern area, and, like the faults, the ore zone crosses the veins at right angles (Fig. 28). This fact alone suggests that the eastward-trending fractures were present at the time of mineralization and helped to localize the ore. The San Rafael vein attains the phenomenal width of 70 m near the Esperanza fault, and the Veta Verde likewise attains its greatest width where crossed by eastward-trending faults.

As the anticline rose and expanded, the direction of stretching was normal to its axis and normal to the walls of the longitudinal vein fractures. The eastward-trending faults lay parallel to the direction of stretching, as did the Canyon fault at Ophir and the great normal fault at Matehuala. Pulling apart of the blocks separated by the San Rafael fault would be greatly expedited if they were free to glide along an eastward-trending fracture. This mechanism might account for the abnormal width of the San Rafael vein near the Esperanza fracture, which later became the locus for postmineral faulting.

No known rock, and least of all thin-bedded shale, could sustain an opening 70 m across. Obviously the San Rafael vein grew here by accretion, the instantaneous filling of relatively small openings as fast as they formed. The vein was a quartz-cemented breccia of shale fragments; the quartz cement showed crustified banding around the rock fragments, and drusy cavities. This structure, plus the great width of the breccia zone, indicates a pulling apart of the adjoining wall rocks as vein matter was deposited.

The solutions that cemented this great body of breccia were those of the earlier type, which formed the gold ore bodies. The axes of these ore bodies were horizontal, and they lay in shale just above the top of the quartz diorite sill in the San Rafael footwall (Figs. 30, 31). There must have been a tendency toward resumption of normal faulting on the San Rafael at this time because innumerable feather-joint branches left the main vein at the horizon of these high-level ore bodies, and contributed to the great width of the vein by the spread of mineralization through the acute angle between the branches and the parent fracture (Fig. 31B).

The thick, strong sill seems to have played a part in making the San Rafael the major vein. The San Rafael fault displaced the sill, before mineralization, in such a manner that one or the other wall of the fault is quartz diorite for a distance down the dip of more than 500 m (Figs. 29, 31). The vein is well defined but not exceptionally wide where either wall is quartz diorite, but it splits and dissipates below the hanging-wall segment of the sill (Fig. 31A). It also pinches out upward in most places not far above the sill (Fig. 31B).

The San Rafael vein is wider in the shale just above the footwall segment of the sill than it is where one wall is quartz diorite. During uplift and lateral stretching the strong sill cracked into a few master breaks such as that of the Descubridora vein (Fig. 31B); the weaker shale above it tended to stretch laterally by flow and minute fracturing. The greatest disruption was along the contact between the yielding shale and the unyielding sill. This may account in part for the great width of the vein here, although the feather joints and, locally, the Esperanza fracture contributed to the widening.

After deposition of the gold ores the mineralizing solutions became richer in precious metals and silver content increased in relation to gold content. These late solutions deposited their ore in low-level feather-joint branches off the San Rafael vein (Fig. 31). The feather joints were gaping as vein matter was deposited as is shown by the banded and drusy structure of these veins. Evidently a tendency toward resumption of fault movements on the San Rafael persisted but was still hindered, and a shearing strain was set up along the fault. It is notable that the high-level feather joints, filled with gold ore, leave the main fault at and above the top of the sill in the footwall of the fault, whereas the low-level feather joints leave where the footwall is quartz diorite or at the top of the hanging-wall segment of the sill (Fig. 31). It seems likely that "tectonic refraction" hindered fault movements, as did the local welding of the fault by early vein matter. A fracture passing from shale into quartz diorite might well suffer "tectonic refraction" and by change of dip acquire one or more jogs in its surface that might hinder further fault movements. Figure 31 suggests the presence of such jogs. The fault is composite in the section of Figure 31A and step faults the sill. Below the sill both faults steepen. Faulting took place, but jogs in the fault surface may well have hindered further movement.

The top of the ore on these low-level feather joints was far below the bottom of the gold ore on the main vein (Figs. 30, 31). Feather joints extend a distance into the walls of their parent fracture corresponding to the outer limit of the tabular block of sheared ground enclosing the parent fracture. Since this outer limit parallels the plane of the parent fracture, each feather joint ends at about the same height above its junction with the parent fracture. Late rich ore-bearing solutions ascending the San Rafael vein through channels as yet unsealed went up along these newly formed low-level feather joints; but, since the latter pinched below the bottom of ore on the main vein, ore on these feather joints lay abnormally deep.

The El Oro anticline appears to plunge northward. It seems likely that during and after the metallization continued uplift, dominantly in the southern portion of the anticline, utilized the eastward-trending fractures as synthetic faults and raised their footwall blocks with reference to sea level. Uplift of the fault footwalls past lagging hanging-wall blocks would explain the relatively large normal displacement on the Esperanza more easily than the contrary assumption—namely, that the hanging-wall block could have dropped by gravity along such a flat and uneven surface.

SOURCES FOR EL ORO: C. B. E. Douglas (1933), unpublished report; Emmons (1937); Flores (1920); W. F. Foshag (1942), unpublished compilation; Hill (1905); Lindgren (1913); Spurr (1923); Winchell (1922)

MOGOLLON, NEW MEXICO

REGIONAL SETTING: The Mogollon silver–gold district lies within the Mogollon volcanic field, on the southeast edge of the Colorado Plateau (Pl. 1). The crystalline basement stands relatively high here.

ROCK FORMATIONS (Tertiary):

Formation	Maximum thickness (Feet)
Ore veins	
Intrusive andesite, diabase	
Dog Gulch formation; conglomerate, sandstone	400+
Mogollon andesite	600
Deadwood Gulch rhyolite tuff	400
Rhyolite dike	
Last Chance andesite (flows, breccias, agglomerate)	600
Fanney rhyolite	1200
Mineral Creek andesite; flows, breccias, agglomerate	700
Pacific quartz latite (flows in upper part of Cranktown sandstone)	700
Houston andesite (flow near base of Cranktown sandstone)	700
Cranktown sandstone	500
Cooney quartz latite (flows, tuffs)	1400
Whitewater Creek rhyolite	700'+

The section contains several erosional unconformities indicating development of a rugged topography between outbursts of volcanism. Owing to these unconformities the thickness of formations varies extremely; the sum of the maxima is about 8000 feet.

STRUCTURE: The major faults—the Queen, Great Western, and Pacific—strike east of north, and dip and downthrow are to the east (Fig. 32). Ferguson's cross sections and regional geologic map (1927, Pls. 2, 3) show that these faults dip toward the core of a large anticline trending and plunging north-northeastward. A compound graben lies along the broad crest. The westward dip of the formations in the Mogollon district and the approximate throw of the Pacific and Queen faults are shown on the near side of the block diagram, which corresponds roughly to Ferguson's Section D-D' of Plate 2.

Whereas the ore district lies on the west flank of a major anticline, it is more closely associated with a superimposed lesser structure.

The structure is a bulge bounded on the east by the Queen fault. The bulge is much more pronounced in northward-trending section (Fig. 32, Section A-A', after Ferguson, 1927, Pl. 2, Section F-F') than in eastward-trending section (Ferguson, 1927, Pl. 2, Section C-C', not shown). Except in the far southern portion of Figure 32 displacement on the Queen fault is at a maximum opposite the crest of the bulge (near the Anaconda eastward-trending vein) and decreases to a minimum opposite the south end of the bulge, in the area of the Last Chance vein.

The Pacific-Great Western fault zone strikingly delineates the bulge. The north and south segments of the fault zone are in perfect alignment, but they do not join because as they approach one another displacements decrease to zero, and the fractures themselves seem to disappear. The gap coincides with the crest of the bulge.

The bulge is fractured and faulted by relatively short eastward-trending breaks. The two southerly breaks, the Last Chance and Maud S, dip northward, whereas the two most important northerly breaks, the Fanney and Anaconda, dip southward. Direction of dip of all four is toward an eastward-trending axis passing through the gap between the Pacific and Great Western faults.

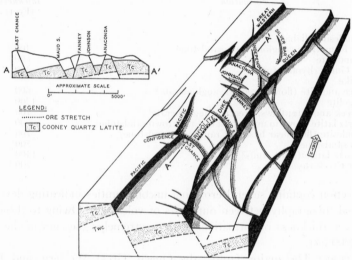

FIGURE 32.—*Block diagram and section, Mogollon district, New Mexico*

ANALYSIS OF STRUCTURE: The relationship of the bulge to the Queen and the Great Western-Pacific faults shows that the major anticline formed before the satellitic upfold. Doubtless these longitudinal faults originated as tension fissures during the major upfolding and were converted to antithetic faults by continued uplift.

The graben area on the crest of the major anticline, east of the Queen fault, was invaded by an andesite stock which enlarges with depth. Intrusion seems to have been forcible, because the extrusive strata turn upward against the sides of the intrusive mass (Ferguson, 1927, Pl. 2 Section C-C'. Possibly the major anticline was created by magmatic pressure, but, if so, the underlying magma sent remarkably few dikes into its cover; the only known one is the rhyolite dike traversing the bulge. Ferguson suggests that this dike fissure, which seems to stand vertically, was the conduit for the Deadwood Gulch rhyolite tuffs, which lie well down in the section. This suggests that the rhyolite dike was intruded long before formulation of the major anticline.

The origin of the bulge is not clear. It has the shape of a doubly plunging anticline trending north-northeastward, and the axis is strongly bowed upward. There is some suggestion that it may have formed above a buried fault in the manner postulated for the doubly plunging satellitic anticlines on flanks of major uplifts in the Big Horn region; if so, the buried fault was longitudinal with respect to the axis of the major anticline, and produced its maximum displacement under the highest part of the satellitic anticline.

Whatever its origin, the bulge seems clearly to have been an autonomous upfold bounded on the east by a pre-existing fault, the Queen, and partly obliterating another pre-existing fault, the Pacific-Great Western.

The bulge stands in relation to the Queen fault somewhat as the Ophir half dome does to the Canyon fault, and the Matehuala half dome to the major fault that bounds it. As the strata in the footwall of the Queen fault were bulged upward, their truncated edges slipped differentially along the footwall surface of the Queen fault and locally increased the original displacement on the fault (Fig. 32).

The eastward-trending faults that break the bulge originated as tension fissures or cross joints normal to the bowed-up axis of this doubly plunging anticline. (Fig. 32, Section A-A'). They lie mainly in the area of southward axial plunge which contains also two cross grabens.

These cross fractures turn on approaching the Queen fault, and tend to join it; this happened because the Queen fault terminated the bulge which produced the cross fractures.

The alignment of the Great Western with the Pacific fault suggests that they were once a single fault, like the Queen fault, and with relatively uniform downdrop on the east. Development of the bulge wiped out part of the fault (Fig. 32).

Unlike the Queen fault on the east, the Pacific-Great Western fault did not confine the bulge on the west; bulging extended westward past the Pacific-Great Western fault (Ferguson, 1927, Pl. 2, Section C-C'). The Confidence-Last Chance antithetic fault created by the bulging cut and displaced the Pacific fault.

METALLIZATION: Both northward-trending and eastward-trending faults and fractures carry veins. The earliest vein mineral was extremely fine-grained quartz with sparse sulfides but practically no gold or silver. Enormous quantities of this early quartz were deposited along the Queen and Great Western faults.

Next came the ore quartz, coarser-grained and drusy, and adularia, fluorite, and calcite. Ore minerals were argentite, stromeyerite, and gold, accompanied by pyrite, chalcopyrite, galena, and sphalerite. The gold–silver ratio was 1:50.

After the ore surge, quartz of the productive type continued to be deposited, but this later surge was low in precious metals and sulfides, and high in fluorite. The final surge of mineralization brought in barren coarsely crystalline manganiferous calcite.

The Queen and Great Western faults carry mainly early quartz and are almost barren of ore. The Pacific fault carried ore only toward its northern end, where it starts to disappear in the bulge (Fig. 32). The eastward-trending fractures that break the bulge received most of the ore of the district.

Ore shoots within the veins were mainly limited to areas where one or both walls are Fanney rhyolite or Mogollon andesite. As with most "bonanza" deposits in Tertiary volcanic rocks, the productive areas in the veins were elongated sub-horizontally. In the Confidence-Last Chance vein the ore shoots lie within an area 5000 feet long horizontally and 700 feet deep.

RELATION OF STRUCTURE TO METALLIZATION: Because postmineral faulting is lacking, displacement on the vein faults was complete before vein formation. The Queen and Great Western faults carry most of the early, fine-grained quartz which is massive, unbroken in these veins. The eastward-trending productive veins carry some of this early quartz, but the quartz type was for the most part that associated with the ore surge. Where ore occurs in barren early quartz, the early quartz has been shattered, and the ore minerals cement the fragments. Metal content in such shoots was diluted below the grade of ore shoots free of barren quartz.

Since they carry some early quartz it is likely that the bulge and its fractures were present at or near the start of mineralization, and that continued bulging caused fractures to gape just in time to receive the ore-bearing solutions. The banded and drusy structure of these veins indicates pulling apart of the walls during the deposition of the ore.

Mogollon illustrates once again the propensity for ore to concentrate in areas of sharp local flexing and consequent stretching of the flexed plates (cf. Ophir, Matehuala, La Plata, Rico, Goldfield, and other districts).

SOURCE FOR MOGOLLON: Ferguson (1927)

OTHER MINING DISTRICTS ASSOCIATED WITH ANTICLINES

Las Damas, Chihuahua, Mexico.—This silver-lead-zinc district is in northern Mexico near where the axis of the Mexican trough existed in Cretaceous time (Pl. 1). The crystalline basement therefore may lie deep here.

Cretaceous limestone has been upfolded into a northward-trending anticline which plunges gently northward. The upfold is sharp (dips on the flanks are almost 60°), but the crest is flattish and is marked by an axial graben. On both sides of the graben longitudinal tension fractures dip toward the axial plane and form a fan pattern in cross section. Fractures of another system strike eastward and dip steeply southward; they lie normal to the northward-plunging axis of the fold (Fig. 1C).

Small replacement ore bodies border the graben on each side and were localized at the intersections of longitudinal and cross fractures with certain limestone beds. Ore formed more extensively along the cross fissures than along those of the other set. Cross fissures open most near the crest of a plunging anticline and disappear down the flanks (data from unpublished reports).

Jarbridge, Nevada.—This minor gold district lies in northeastern Nevada on the border between the Great Basin on the south and the Snake River downwarp on the north. It is situated above a marked structural high in the crystalline basement (Pl. 1).

Rhyolite flows aggregating 6000 feet in thickness have been upfolded to form a gentle anticline trending west of north and plunging gently northward. Rhyolite dikes invaded longitudinal tension fissures, probably during an early stage of arching.

Continued although still gentle arching produced a long, narrow zone of persistent normal faults along the eastern flank of the anticline near the crest. The faults dip westward and have dropped the crestal portion of the anticline.

A second broader belt of fractures lies west of the crest. The fractures strike with the anticlinal axis and dip eastward toward it. Individual fractures are less persistent than those of the eastern belt, and faulting is slight or lacking along them. The structure along the crest of the anticline is that of a half graben; faulting is east of the axis, and only fissuring is west of it.

Fractures of a third set strike perpendicular to the anticlinal axis and dip steeply southward normal to the axis of the northward-plunging anticline. They are cross joints.

Fractures of all three sets carry veins. The gold–silver ore was mainly oxidized, but residual sulfides included argentite and pyrite. The gangue consisted of quartz, adularia, apatite, barite, fluorite, and calcite.

Veins along the eastern fault zone are narrow and carry gouge along their footwalls and within the vein. Production was scanty from this zone; the bulk of it came from the fissures of the western belt where gouge was lacking and the vein matter was frozen to the walls. Several cross fractures carried ore; the most important of these was the Buster vein which carried gouge along both walls and within the vein. Like many cross fractures, it was faulted (Schrader, 1923).

Ocampo, Chihuahua, Mexico.—This important silver–gold district lies on the western slope of the Sierra Madre Occidental within the great lava field constituting most of that cordillera. The axis of the late Cretaceous Occidental geanticline passed through what is now Ocampo. The crystalline basement probably lies high, compared to its position east and west of the geanticline.

Andesite flows and tuffs with interbedded rhyolite flows and tuffs have been upfolded into a large anticline trending northwestward; the Ocampo district occupies part of the northeast limb. Andesite dikes strike northwestward, parallel with the axis of the fold, and dip southwestward toward the axial plane. They fill tension fissures produced at an early stage of arching. Faulting followed fissuring; the faults parallel the dikes in strike and dip and step fault the eastward-dipping bedded volcanic rocks with downthrow toward the crest of the fold.

The principal ore bodies lay along these faults. Silver occurred as argentite and stephanite in a quartz gangue. Minor tetrahedrite, sphalerite, and galena were present. The gold–silver ratio was 1:60.

Apparently metallization took place after most or all of the faulting had been effected and when "locking" of the antithetic fault blocks prevented further fault movement. As at Guanajuato, lesser veins along fissures of no displacement show crustified banding and druses. The fault veins in places were composed of quartz-cemented rock rubble; where mineralization was so intense as to replace the boulders, ore bodies were formed. Elsewhere the fault veins are mineralized sheeted zones (Linton, 1912; Emmons, 1937; unpublished reports).

Quartz Hill, Montana.—This silver district is 30 miles south-southwest of Butte. The basement lies at relatively shallow depth here because Precambrian crystalline rocks crop out only a few miles to the east and west (Pl. 1).

Black limestone overlies shale which in turn overlies crystalline limestone (Fig. 33). These Paleozoic strata have been upfolded into a northwest-trending anticline or elongate dome cut by numerous nearly vertical cross joints and by several longitudinal fissures.

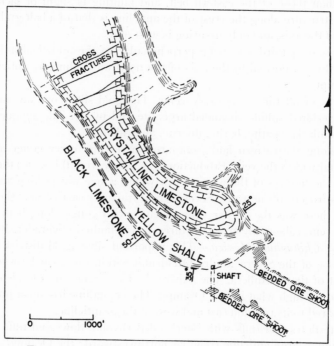

FIGURE 33.—*Structural map, Quartz Hill district, Montana*

Taylor (1942, p. 212) recognized the genetic relation between these epi-anticlinal fractures and the doming.

The cross joints and longitudinal fissures are strongly developed in the crystalline limestone but branch and disappear in the overlying shale, like similar fissures at Rico which dissipate on entering the soft Newman Hill "blanket." The fissures opened widest directly beneath the shale, which served as a lubricant to facilitate gliding of the top edge of the limestone each way from a cross-joint plane of parting.

Silver occurred as freibergite in a gangue of quartz, barite, and calcite. The ore bodies were pipes in the cross joints, and bedded replacement deposits were localized by longitudinal fissures at the contact of the crystalline limestone with the overlying shale. Neither type of ore penetrated the shale.

Ore on the cross joints was localized just below the shale capping where the fissure opened widest. The ore tended to mushroom below the shale by replacing the limestone for short distances on each side of the cross joint. The pipes pitched downward along the lines of intersection of the cross joints with the base of the shale (Taylor, 1942).

Catorce, San Luis Potosi, Mexico.—Catorce, a major silver producer, is 20 km west of Matehuala (Pl. 1). The axis of the Mexican trough passed through this area in the Early Cretaceous, but the basement must lie relatively high here today, because Catorce lies near the apex of a domical uplift with Paleozoic rocks in its core.

At Catorce Upper Jurassic conglomerate overlies schist and slaty shale and is overlain by sandstone grading upward to shale. Above the shale lies the ore-bearing limestone, also Jurassic in age, overlain by Jurassic and Lower Cretaceous limestones.

The strata have been upfolded into a doubly plunging anticline or elongate dome superimposed on the east flank of the major dome. The satellitic fold trends north-northwestward and plunges northward. It carries both longitudinal and cross fractures. The longitudinal fractures dip toward the axial plane of the anticline and form a fan pattern in cross section.

Quartz monzonite dikes were intruded along fractures of both sets, and a diorite plug intrudes the crestal part of the uplift; it was shoved forcibly up through the strata, which turn up around it.

Both fracture systems contain normal faults, and a graben lies near the apex of the uplift; whether the graben is bounded by longitudinal or cross faults or by faults of both sets, Baker, who describes it (1922, p. 45), does not say.

Ore minerals included argentite and ruby silvers; other metallic minerals were stibnite, sulfides of arsenic and bismuth, galena, sphalerite, chalcopyrite, and pyrite. The gangue is calcite, quartz, and rhodonite.

The chief ore shoots lay in the ore-bearing limestone at intersections of longitudinal fractures with cross-fractures. Their shape was pipelike; the major axes followed the lines of intersection of fractures of the two sets. Obviously the limestone was stretched in two directions during upfolding; one stretch was caused by bending around the anticlinal axis to produce longitudinal fissures, the other caused by upbending of the axis itself to create cross fissures (Fig. 1).

Baker, a petroleum geologist, expresses astonishment in his paper on Catorce that all ore districts seen by him in northeastern Mexico are located like oil fields, on anticlinal structures and usually in their crestal portions where open spaces are most likely to occur because of flexing of brittle strata (Baker, 1922; C. B. E. Douglas, 1936, personal communication).

SUMMARY AND CONCLUSIONS
RELATION OF ORE DEPOSITION TO UPLIFT

The 18 ore districts described, and 89 others shown on Plate 1, exhibit enough similarities to suggest the following generalizations:

(1) Uplift, whether apical or axial, was accompanied from the beginning by development of tension fissures many of which were immediately filled by dikes (La Plata, Rico, Creede, Antelope, El Oro, Guanajuato, Jarbridge, Ocampo). Dike invasion at Sunlight, Kirwin, and Silverton was probably also an accompaniment of uplift.

(2) The strata involved in formation of these "blisters" were relatively competent: volcanic flows, indurated pyroclastic rocks, limestone, quartzite. In most cases the dome or anticline produced was gentle. Although deformation was comparatively slight, fissures formed readily owing to the relative weakness of rock under tension. The fissured rock, however, was strong enough to "bridge" the fissures—*i.e.*, to keep them open under persistent uplift.

(3) Uplift frequently was accompanied by intrusion of stocks or batholiths (Sunlight, Kirwin, Silverton, Matehuala, La Plata, Rico, Guanajuato, Mogollon).

(4) Mineralizing solutions usually entered a deforming area soon after emplacement of the last intrusive type which commonly took the form of dikes. Uplift and consequent stretching of the domed or arched plate persisted through the period of metallization, but by this time stretching had in many places reached a stage where fissuring could no longer accommodate it, and its final stages were achieved by graben and antithetic faulting. Ore deposition sometimes preceded this faulting (Antelope), sometimes accompanied it at least in part (Bodie); more often ore deposition followed faulting (Silverton, La Plata, Rico, Goldfield, Creede, El Oro, Guanajuato, Mogollon, Jarbridge, Ocampo).

(5) Where the period of mineralization persisted past that of major faulting, continued uplift sometimes created a tendency toward renewal of fault movement. Where for one or another reason such renewal was prevented or hindered, the shearing strain set up along the faults was relieved by ripping open of the wall rocks to form feather joints, many of which became loci for ore (Arrastre Basin, Silverton, Goldfield, Creede, El Oro). At Guanajuato hindrance to fault movement on the Veta Madre created stockworks in the hanging wall, and these were mineralized to form ore bodies.

(6) The fracture pattern on these domes and anticlines developed progressively as uplift continued. Solutions deposited vein matter in those fractures available at the time, and so situated as to be reachable from the main solution channel. Burbank has demonstrated this for Silverton.

(7) Ore-bearing solutions often appear to have utilized peripheries of stocks as channels for ascent (Sunlight, Kirwin, Matehuala, Silverton, La Plata, Guanajuato).

(8) Master fractures also seem to have served as trunk channels for ore solutions (Goldfield, Creede, El Oro, Mogollon, and other districts).

99

DISTRIBUTION OF THE ORE DISTRICTS
IN THE CORDILLERAN REGION

If tectonic concepts developed in the present work are valid, ore districts related to structures produced by vertical forces are distributed throughout the Cordillera (Pl. 1). They are widely distributed in time as well, ranging in age from Nevadan (Star Peak, Nevada, not described but shown on Pl. 1) to Pliocene (Bodie).

If, however, these ore districts, classified according to their structural settings, are further classified according to their mineral assemblages and other features, their distribution varies according to the categories into which they fall.

Dissatisfaction is developing over the Lindgren physico-chemical classification of hypogene ore deposits (Schmitt, 1950b, p. 672). The epithermal class of Lindgren is nevertheless a well-defined entity and has few borderline members such as the other groups exhibit. It seems safe, therefore, for the present purpose to group the ore districts shown on Plate 1 merely into epithermal and nonepithermal deposits.

According to Schmitt (1950a, p. 192-193, 198) the following features are virtually restricted to epithermal deposits: crustified, drusy, hackly, and colloform texture; presence of potassium, barium, and fluorine in the gangue, and of tellurium, selenium, arsenic, antimony, bismuth, and mercury among the metallic elements. Pyrite and base sulfides as a rule are not abundant. Vein deposits predominate, and many of them follow faults of notable displacement. Epithermal deposits also may be largely restricted to Tertiary time. Deposits which do not show these characteristics are classified as nonepithermal.

DISTRIBUTION OF NONEPITHERMAL DEPOSITS (Pl. 1, Table 1): These deposits, grouped areally, appear to be of about the same age and to share common characteristics.

In areal relation to the Idaho batholith are Gibbonsville (No. 2; gold, massive pyrite), Philipsburg (No. 1; gold, pyrite), and Buffalo Hump (No. 3; base metals). The Quartz Hill silver deposit and the Blue Wing (Ima) tungsten-base metal deposit lie in this area. The anticlines with which these deposits are associated were presumably upfolded in Laramide time, and the ore deposits date from the same period.

The Star Peak anticline in the Great Basin and its associated silver-gold-antimony deposits lie within the region apparently metallized during the Nevadan orogeny.

The Contact and Bullion silver-lead-copper districts in northeastern Nevada, which are also associated with anticlines, lie in an area where metallization accompanied orogeny which may date from Mid-Cretaceous time or be as late as early Tertiary.

The anticlines and base-metal ores of Galena Mountain (No. 17) and Mount Lincoln (No. 23) in Colorado probably date from Laramide time.

The following ore districts show a peripheral relation to the Colorado Plateau: Ophir (half dome; lead-silver); Park City (on east flank of Cotton-

wood dome; silver-lead-zinc); Cerillos (laccolithic dome; silver-lead-zinc);
Magdalena (No. 19; anticline; zinc) : Central district (No. 20; anticlines, domes,
basins; iron-zinc-copper); Johnson (dome; copper-zinc); Apache (No. 22;
anticline; iron) ; Bagdad (No. 15; dome; copper).

In Mexico a few nonepithermal deposits lie along the Late Cretaceous site of
the Occidental geanticline; Cananea (No. 27; anticline; copper); Oposura (No.
32; dome; zinc); Guanynopita (No. 33; dome; silver-copper-gold).

A belt of nonepithermal deposits associated with upfolds lies along the axis
of the Early Cretaceous Mexican trough: Sabinal (No. 29; dome; silver-lead);
Las Damas (anticline; silver-lead); Los Lamentos (half dome; silver-lead);
Santa Eulalia (gentle dome; silver-lead-zinc-tin); Velardeña (No. 48; anticline; copper, massive pyrite); Catorce (anticline; silver-base metals; epithermal?) ; Matehuala (half dome; copper) ; San Pedro (No. 63; dome; lead-silver).

On the Coahuila platform and in or near the Coahuila and Parras troughs lie
the following lead-silver or lead-silver-zinc deposits, all associated with isolated
anticlines: Boquillas (No. 34); Santa Elena (No. 38); Minas Viejas (No. 42);
Mitra Mountain (No. 46); Higueras (No. 45); Mier y Noriega (No. 60); San
Nicolás (No. 51). The San Jose copper deposit (No. 50; west of San Nicolás)
is associated with a dome.

These Mexican nonepithermal deposits probably date from periods ranging
from Late Cretaceous to Early Tertiary.

DISTRIBUTION OF EPITHERMAL DEPOSITS: In contrast to the areal-temporal
groupings of the nonepithermal deposits associated with anticlines and domes,
epithermal deposits all probably dating from mid-Tertiary or later time are
scattered from one end of the Cordilleran region to the other. They show, however, a preference for major uplifts and an avoidance of fossil geosynclinal
troughs.

Plate 1 attempts to show the topography of the crystalline basement surface
in the Cordilleran region. Outcrops of Precambrian rocks indicate regions of
maximum uplift. The line surrounding stippled areas is the contour of the surface
at 5000 feet below sea level and indicates maximum depression; the more intense
the stippling the deeper is the depressed area.

The structural picture is that of today; but since epithermal deposits are of
relatively recent age and because major deformations since their formation were
mainly epeirogenic, the structure portrayed may be considered to be that existent
at the time of formation of these deposits.

The principal fossil trough in western United States is that of the Cordilleran
geosyncline, active from the Late Precambrian but reaching its greatest development in the Early Paleozoic. The trough trended southeastward in Canada and
crossed the border as a broad belt extending from northeastern Washington to
central Montana. It persisted southeastward to the latitude of the present Idaho
batholith (which lies on the western edge of the trough) and thence swerved
southwestward through northwest Utah and most of Nevada, reaching the
Pacific as a wide trough embracing most of the southern two-thirds of California.

The great area of depressed basement shown in Plate 1 between the Sierra Nevada batholith and the Colorado Plateau depicts a segment of this fossil trough. Precambrian rocks cropping out southeast of the Sierra Nevada batholith lie athwart the course of the former trough and show that the depressed area was strongly uplifted at some relatively recent period, but before formation of Cordilleran epithermal deposits.

The epithermal districts of Jarbridge, Tuscarora, and Seven Troughs, all associated with anticlines, lie along the northwest edge of the ancient trough. Bodie lies within the trough but close to the post-trough Sierra Nevada massive. Goldfield, Tonopah (No. 9), and Antelope lie directly or obliquely above relative highs in the trough. The basement may lie deep beneath Bullfrog (No. 12), but Mohave (No. 13) Calico, and Oatman (No. 14) are situated on the uplift that wiped out the southwestern portion of the trough. Where the trough remains deeply buried, epithermal deposits are almost lacking.

In the eastern portion of the Cordillera, Sunlight and Kirwin lie in a strongly uplifted area; outcrops of Precambrian crystalline rocks are found close to these districts. Silverton, Rico, La Plata, Creede, and Bonanza (No. 18) in the San Juan region are located on a tectonic element persistently positive since the end of the Paleozoic.

The crystalline basement is undoubtedly high at Mogollon.

In Mexico epithermal deposits avoid the Mexican fossil trough but are extremely abundant along the persistently positive Occidental geanticline.

Since each of the epithermal deposits shown in Plate 1 is associated with a local uplift, it is not surprising to find them related also to regional uplifts.

RELATION OF EPITHERMAL DEPOSITS TO DEVELOPMENT OF THE CORDILLERA

The enormous areal distribution of epithermal deposits in the Cordilleran region suggests a relation between this type of ore deposition and the Cordillera as a whole or at least those major portions of it which have been strongly uplifted. The deformation with which the epithermal deposits are associated was not only subcontinental in scope but must have been deep-seated as well.

The average depth of the sedimentary cover within the Cordilleran region is presently about 1.5 miles. Since the last great epoch of sedimentation, in the Late Cretaceous, erosion has probably roughly balanced sedimentation so that the cover has been about 1.5 miles thick ever since that time.

Beneath the sedimentary cover, the granitic layer or sial probably averages about 20 miles thick. The depth to the bottom of the crystalline crust may be on the order of 43 miles. The thickness of the cover, therefore, is 3.4 per cent of the thickness of the crust.

Obviously the sedimentary cover is a mere veneer; in a deformation embracing the Cordilleran region as a whole the major role would be played by the crystalline crust, whereas the cover would merely reflect the deformation beneath it. Fractures capable of tapping magma and ore sources at depth must have originated in the competent sial from which they worked upward into the relatively incompetent cover.

Not only are the epithermal deposits of the Cordilleran region associated spatially with major uplifts; they are associated genetically as well, for the uplifts were still developing during metallization, and the Cordillera was fast assuming its present shape. Thus the local phenomena of uplift, stretching, fissuring, intrusion, and metallization which characterize the epithermal ore districts described were satellitic features superimposed on major uplifts or even upon one gigantic uplift, that of the Cordilleran region as a whole.

Owing to the complexity of the Cordilleran region in the United States the last supposition may be questioned. Figure 34 compares the present appearance

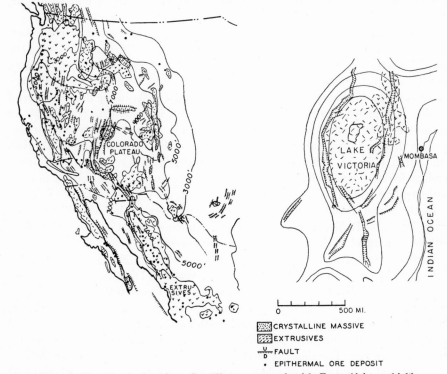

FIGURE 34.—*North American Cordillera compared with East African shield*

of the Cordilleran region of western North America with that of the East African shield (H. Cloos, 1939, Pl. II, III). The East African shield is an elongated structural dome, on which are axial grabens deflected from their normal course by the resistant crystalline core. Where the dome plunges to the south the grabens radiate in the manner of many small-scale examples described in the present work. Volcanism accompanied the uplift; the magma ascended the tensional graben fault zones.

North and south of the United States the Cordilleran uplift is geanticlinal in shape and is far more linear than that of the East African shield. Major fractures are longitudinal and trend parallel to the axis of uplift. Volcanism in general was coextensive with the crestal portion of the geanticline, and the great bulk of epithermal deposits in Mexico lies upon this crestal portion also.

In the United States the Colorado Plateau formed a resistant core corresponding to the crystalline core of the East African shield. Basin-and-range faulting avoids the core, and the fault zones, as in the East African shield, trend to drape themselves around the periphery of the core; volcanic fields, minor intrusions, and ore deposits show the same relation to the Plateau.

Thus whereas the North American Cordillera is more complex than the East African shield, both structurally and historically, the final deformation of the former was, like that of the East African shield, tectonically a unit taking the form of a broad, integrated epeirogenic uplift.

Whereas the basin-and-range faults in the Cordilleran region reached their present development mainly after formation of the epithermal deposits, the essential fracture pattern was in existence at the time of epithermal metallization. Indeed, perhaps the most striking feature brought out by Plate 1 is the persistence of structural grain through geologic ages. In the Great Basin the dominant trend of folds is roughly northward, and the secondary is eastward. These folds in sedimentary strata antedate epithermal metallization; many ore districts that also antedate that metallization seem related in time to this folding—Star Peak, Bullion, Cortez, (No. 5), White Pine (No. 8), among districts related to northward-trending folds; Contact and Park Valley (No. 4), among those related to eastward-trending folds).

In the Great Basin epithermal deposits, fractures at Jarbidge, Tuscarora, Seven Troughs, Bodie, Tonopah (No. 9), Antelope, and Calico trend mainly northward, parallel to the basin-and-range fault system.

Persistence of structural grain is still more evident in Mexico where almost all the anticlines associated with epithermal deposits trend northwestward, parallel to the axis of the Mexican trough and to that of the Occidental geanticline. Furthermore, in at least two and probably many more cases, folding of sediments, which antedates Tertiary volcanism and epithermal metallization, was resumed during that metallization; the older fold was revived and accentuated (Los Reyes, Cabacera—No. 49). The simplest mechanism to account for revival of an isolated fold is renewal of movement of a basement fault which produced the original fold in the manner suggested for the Big Horn region.

DEPTH OF ORIGIN OF EPITHERMAL ORES

Pointing out the association of epithermal deposits with volcanism, Lindgren states (1933, p. 445) : "It would seem logical to suggest that the epithermal veins were formed from hot solutions which had their origin in the deep reservoirs where the magma was differentiated into the various types of flow rocks, and not, like most mesothermal and hypothermal deposits, in batholithic deposits nearer the surface."

A deep-seated origin for epithermal ores is suggested by the following considerations:

(1) They did not appear until the complex Cordilleran uplift had almost reached its maximum development, at which time they were emplaced from one end of the uplift to the other.

(2) Tension fissures reach their greatest length and depth where produced by broad, shieldlike uplifts such as those with which the Cordilleran epithermal deposits are spatially and genetically associated.

(3) In areas of strong uplift it may be presumed that lower crustal layers and layers that lie beneath the crust are abnormally close to the surface of the earth. Much of the crystalline basement was eroded from the San Juan uplift before formation of the epithermal deposits there. Thus major uplifts, through crustal stretching, produced tension fissures that extended to abnormal depths, whereas at the same time the crustal and lower layers lay abnormally high. Conditions were ideal for tapping a very deep source of magma and ore.

(4) Epithermal deposits have a relatively uniform mineralogic makeup in contrast to strong local variations in other types of deposits. This uniform makeup and the extremely wide distribution of epithermal deposits suggests a deep-seated, uniform source for the ores.

REFERENCES CITED

ANDERSON, A. L. (1948) *Tungsten mineralization at the Ima mine, Blue Wing district, Lemhi Co., Idaho,* Econ. Geol., v. 43, p. 181-206

ANDERSON, C. A. (1948) *Structural control of copper mineralization, Bagdad, Arizona,* Am. Inst. Min. Met. Engrs. Trans., v. 178, p. 170-180

————— (1950) *Alteration and metallization in the Bagdad porphyry copper deposit, Arizona,* Econ. Geol., v. 45, p. 609-628

ANDERSON, E. M. (1937) *Cone sheets and ring dikes; the dynamical explanation,* Bull. Volcanogique, v. I (2nd ser., 1937), p. 35-40

ANONYMOUS (1917) *Informe sobre el mineral de Sierra del Carmen* (Boquillas), Boletin Minero, Feb., p. 97-101

ANONYMOUS (1922) *Hornsilver district, Nevada,* Min. Sci. Press, Jan. 21, p. 93-94

ARGALL, PHILIP (1908) *Ore deposits of Magdalena, New Mexico,* Engr. Min. Jour., v. 86, p. 366-370

ATWOOD, W. W., AND MATHER, K. F. (1932) *Physiography and Quaternary geology of the San Juan Mountains, Colorado,* U. S. Geol. Survey Prof. Paper 166, p. 15, 18

BAKER, ARTHUR III (1953) *Location of pyrometasomatic ore deposits at Johnson Camp, Arizona,* Am. Inst. Min. Met. Engrs. Trans., v. 196, p. 1272-1277

BAKER, C. L. (1922) *General geology of Catorce mining district, Mexico,* Am. Inst. Min. Met. Engrs. Trans., v. 46, p. 42-48

BALK, ROBERT (1937) *Structural behavior of igneous rocks,* Geol. Soc. Am. Mem. 5, p. 27-33

BALL, MAX W. (1921) *Relative ages of major and minor folding and oil accumulation in Wyoming,* Am. Assoc. Petrol. Geol. Bull., v. 5, p. 49-63

BALL, S. H. (1907) *Geological reconnaissance in southwestern Nevada and eastern California,* U. S. Geol. Survey Bull. 308, p. 89-95

BARRERA, TOMÁS (1931) *Zonas mineras de los estados de Jalisco y Nayarit,* Instituto Geológico de México Bol. 51, p. 53-60

BASTIN, E. S. (1937) *Ore deposits of San Carlos Mountains,* Mich. Univ. Sci. ser., v. 12, p. 163-185, 187-197

BATESON, C. W. (1907) *Mohave mining district, California,* Am. Inst. Min. Met. Engrs. Trans., v. 37, p. 160-177

BECKWITH, R. H. (1928) *Geology and ore deposits of the Buffalo Hump district* (Idaho), N. Y. Acad. Sci. Annals, v. 30, p. 263-296

BERG, GEORG (1932) *Vein filling during the opening of fissures,* Econ. Geol., v. 27, p. 87-94

BOUTWELL, J. M. (1912) *Geology and ore deposits of Park City, Utah,* U. S. Geol. Survey Prof. Paper 77, 231 p.

BRODIE, W. M. (1909) *The native silver mines of Batopilas,* Mining World, v. 30, p. 1201-1208

BROWN, R. GILMAN (1907) *Vein systems of the Standard mine, Bodie, California,* Am. Inst. Min. Met. Engrs. Trans., v. 38, p. 343-357

BUCHER, WALTER H. (1933) *Deformation of the earth's crust,* Princeton Univ. Press, p. 145, 338

BURBANK, W. S. (1932) *Geology and ore deposits of the Bonanza mining district, Colorado,* U. S. Geol. Survey Prof. Paper 169, 166 p.

————— (1933) *Vein systems in the Arrastre Basin and regional geologic structure in the Silverton and Telluride quadrangles, Colorado,* Colo. Sci. Soc. Proc., v. 13, no. 5, p. 136-215

————— (1940) *Structural control of ore deposition in the Uncompahgre district, Ouray Co., Colorado,* U. S. Geol. Survey Bull. 906E, p. 190-265

————— (1941) *Structural control of ore deposition in the Red Mountain, Sneffels and Telluride districts of the San Juan Mountains, Colorado,* Colo. Sci. Soc. Proc., v. 14, no. 5, p. 141-261

————— (1947) *Districts of the Silverton volcanic center,* in *Mineral Resources of Colorado,* State of Colorado Mineral Resources Board, Denver, p. 419-424

BUTLER, B. S. (1914) *Notes on the Unaweep copper district, Colorado,* U. S. Geol. Survey Bull. 580R, p. 19-23

BUTLER, B. S., et al. (1920), *Ore deposits of Utah,* U. S. Geol. Survey Prof. Paper 111, p. 376

CALLAGHAN, EUGENE, AND LEMMON, DWIGHT M. (1941) *Tungsten resources of the Blue Wing district, Lemhi Co., Idaho,* U. S. Geol. Survey Bull. 931A, p. 1-21

CAMERON, E. N. (1939) *Geology and mineralization of the northwestern Humboldt Range, Nevada (Star Peak district),* Geol. Soc. Am. Bull., v. 50, p. 563-634

CLOOS, ERNST (1932) *"Feather joints" as indicators of movements on faults, joints, thrusts and magmatic contacts,* Nat. Acad. Sci. Proc., v. 18, p. 387-395

———— (1955) *Experimental analysis of fracture patterns,* Geol. Soc. Am. Bull., v. 66, p. 241-256

CLOOS, ERNST, AND CLOOS, HANS (1934) *Precambrian structure of the Beartooth, the Big Horn, and the Black Hills uplifts and its coincidence with Tertiary uplifting* (abstract), Geol. Soc. Am. Proc. 1933, p. 56

CLOOS, HANS (1928) *Ueber antithetische Bewegungen,* Geol. Rundschau, Bd. 19, Heft 3, p. 246-251

———— (1939) *Hebung, Spaltung, Vulkanismus,* Geol. Rundschau, Bd. 30, Heft 4A, p. 405-527

COLLINS, GEORGE E. (1931) *Localization of ore bodies at Rico and Red Mountain, Colorado,* Colo. Sci. Soc. Proc., v. 12, p. 407-424

CROSS, WHITMAN (1899) *La Plata Folio,* U. S. Geol. Survey, Folio no. 60, 14 p.

CROSS, WHITMAN, AND HOWE, ERNEST (1905) *Silverton Folio,* U. S. Geol. Survey, Folio no. 120, p. 11, 23

———— (1907) *Ouray Folio,* U. S. Geol. Survey, Folio no. 153, p. 11

CROSS, WHITMAN, AND LARSEN, E. S., *Brief review of the geology of the San Juan region of Southwestern Colorado,* U. S. Geol. Survey Bull. 843, p. 110

CROSS, WHITMAN, AND SPENCER, A. C. (1900) *Geology of the Rico Mountains, Colorado,* U. S. Geol. Survey, 21st Ann. Rept., II, p. 7-165

DANE, C. H., AND ROSS, C. P. (1942) *Wild Horse quicksilver district, Lander Co., Nevada,* U. S. Geol. Survey Bull. 931K, p. 259-278

DE KALB, COURTENAY (1908) *Geology of the Exposed Treasure lode, Mojave, California,* Am. Inst. Min. Engrs. Trans., v. 39, p. 310-319

DONALD, R. T. (1935) *Geological study at Cusi reveals new ore,* Engr. Min. Jour., v. 136, p. 614-617

EARDLEY, A. J. (1939) *Structure of the Wasatch-Great Basin region,* Geol. Soc. Am. Bull., v. 50, p. 1277-1310

ECKEL, E. B. (1936) *Resurvey of geology and ore deposits of La Plata mining district, Colorado,* Colo. Sci. Soc. Proc., v. 13, no. 9, p. 507-547

———— (1949) *Geology and ore deposits of La Plata district, Colorado,* U. S. Geol. Survey Prof. Paper 219, p. 47

EKKERNKAMP, M. (1939) *Zum Problem der aelteren Anlagen in Bruchgebieten,* Geol. Rundschau, Bd. 30, Heft 7-8, p. 713-764

EMMONS, W. H. (1910) *Reconnaissance of some mining camps in Elko, Lander and Eureka Counties, Nevada,* U. S. Geol. Survey Bull. 408, p. 59-62, 88-99

———— (1937) *Gold deposits of the world,* McGraw-Hill Book Co., Inc., N. Y., p. 227

EMMONS, W. H., AND CALKINS, F. C. (1913) *Geology and ore deposits of Philipsburg quadrangle, Montana,* U. S. Geol. Survey Prof. Paper 78, 271 p.

EMMONS, W. H., AND GARREY, G. H. (1910), section on *Mechanics of the deformation,* in *Geology and ore deposits of the Bullfrog district, Nevada,* U. S. Geol. Survey Bull. 407, p. 81-89

EMMONS, W. H., AND LARSEN, E. S. (1923) *Geology and ore deposits of the Creede quadrangle, Colorado,* U. S. Geol. Survey Bull. 718, 193 p.

ESPACH, R. H., AND NICHOLS, H. D. (1914) *Petroleum and natural gas fields in Wyoming,* U. S. Bur. Mines Bull. 418, Sheet 3, Figure 9 (Big Muddy Oil Field)

FERGUSON, H. G. (1927) *Geology and ore deposits of the Mogollon mining district, New Mexico,* U. S. Geol. Survey Bull. 787, p. 93-94, 150

FLETCHER, A. R. (1929) *Mexico's lead-silver manto deposits and their origin,* Engr. Min. Jour., v. 127, p. 509-513

FLORES, T. (1920) *Estudio geológico-minero de los distritos de El Oro y Tlalpujahua,* Inst. Geológico Mexicano, Bol. 37, p. 1-85

FOSHAG, W. F. (1927) *Quicksilver deposits of the Pilot Mountains, Mineral Co., Nevada,* U. S. Geol. Survey Bull. 795E, p. 113-123

———— (1934) *Ore deposits of Los Lamentos, Chihuahua, Mexico,* Econ. Geol., v. 29, p. 330-345

GILLULY, JAMES (1932) *Geology and ore deposits of the Stockton and Fairfield quadrangles, Utah,* U. S. Geol. Survey Prof. Paper 173, p. 69, 78-79, 150

GODDARD, E. N. (1940) *Manganese deposits at Philipsburg, Granite Co., Montana,* U. S. Geol. Survey Bull. 922G, p. 157-204

GONZALEZ REYNA, J. (1956) *Riqueza minera yacimientos minerales de México,* Banco de México, S.A., Departmento de Investigaciones Industriales, 3rd ed., p. 154-159

GOUBKIN, I. M. (1934) *Tectonics of southeastern Caucasus and its relation to productive oil fields,* Am. Assoc. Petrol. Geol. Bull., v. 18, p. 603-671

GREENAN, J. O. (1927) *The Cortez district rejuvenated,* Engr. Min. Jour., v. 124, p. 413-416

HARRISON, T. S. (1927) *Colorado-Utah salt domes,* Am. Assoc. Petrol. Geol. Bull., v. 11-1, p. 111-133

HAYWARD, M. W., AND TRIPLETT, W. H. (1931) *Occurrence of lead-zinc ores in dolomitic limestones in northern Mexico,* Am. Inst. Min. Met. Engrs. Tech. Publ. 442, p. 15-17, 27-28

HEWETT, D. F. (1914) *Ore deposits of Kirwin, Wyoming,* U. S. Geol. Survey Bull. 540, p. 121-132

HEWITT, W. P. (1943) *Geology and mineralization of the San Antonio mine, Santa Eulalia district, Chihuahua, Mexico,* Geol. Soc. Am. Bull., v. 54, p. 173-204

HILL, R. T. (1905) *El Oro district, Mexico,* Engr. Min. Jour., Mar. 2, p. 410-413

HILLS, E. SHERBON (1941) *Outlines of structural geology,* Nordeman Publishing Co., Inc., N. Y., p. 65, 122-124

HOVEY, E. O. (1906) *Geology of the Guaynopita district, Chihuahua,* Festschrift, Harry Rosenbusch, Stuttgart, p. 77-95

HUBBELL, A. H. (1927) *Rico revived,* Engr. Min. Jour., v. 123, p. 317-321

HULIN, C. D. (1929) *Structural control of ore deposition,* Econ. Geol., v. 24, p. 15-49

HUMMEL, C. L. (1952) *Structure and mineralization of a portion of the Bald Mountain mining district, South Dakota* (Abstract), Geol. Soc. Bull., v. 63, p. 1364

IRELAN, WM. JR. (1888) *Section on Bodie,* in State Mineralogist's 8th Annual Report, p. 382-400

IRWIN, J. S. (1926) *Faulting in the Rocky Mountain region,* Am. Assoc. Petrol. Geol. Bull., v. 10, p. 105-129

———— (1929) *Oil and gas fields of Lost Soldier district, Wyoming,* in *Structure of typical American oil fields, II,* Am. Assoc. Petrol. Geol., Tulsa, Okla., p. 636-666

JOHNSON, DOUGLAS (1903) *Geology of the Cerillos Hills, New Mexico,* (Columbia) School of Mines Quarterly, v. 24, pt. I, *General geology,* p. 303-350, 456-500

KELLEY, V. C. (1937) *Geology of the Darwin silver-lead deposits,* Econ. Geol., v. 32, p. 987-1008

———— (1946) *Geology, ore deposits and mines of the Mineral Point, Poughkeepsie and Upper Uncompahgre districts, San Juan and Hinsdale Counties, Colorado,* Colo. Sci. Soc. Proc., v. 14, no. 7, p. 287-466

KNAPP, M. A. (1906) *The fault system of eastern Santa Eulalia*, Engr. Min. Jour., v. 81, p. 993-994

KRIEGER, PHILIP (1935) *Primary silver mineralization at Sabinal, Chihuahua*, Econ. Geol., v. 30, p. 242-259

LARSEN, E. S. (1929) *Recent developments in the Creede district, Colorado*, U. S. Geol. Survey Bull. 811, p. 89-112

LARSH, W. S. (1909) *Mining at Hamilton, Nevada; geology of the White Pine district*, Mines and Minerals, v. 29, p. 521-523

LASKY, S. G. (1936) *Geology and ore deposits of Bayard area, Central mining district, New Mexico*, U. S. Geol. Survey Bull. 870, 144 p.

LAUSEN, CARL (1931) *Geology and ore deposits of Oatman and Katherine districts, Arizona*, Arizona Bur. Mines Geol. ser. 6, Bull. 131, 126 p.

LEITH, C. K. (1923) *Structural geology*, revised ed., Henry Holt & Co., N. Y., p. 288-292

LEWIS, S. J. (1920) *Ore deposits of Mexico II*, Min. Sci. Press, Mar. 27, p. 444-446

LINCOLN, F. C. (1911) *Some gold deposits of the northwest*, Engr. Min. Jour., v. 92, p. 408-410

LINDGREN, W. (1887) *The silver mines of Calico, California*, Am. Inst. Min. Engrs. Trans., v. 15, p. 717-734

———— (1933) *Mineral deposits*, McGraw-Hill Book Co., Inc., N. Y., 445 p.

LINDGREN, W., GRATON, L. C., AND GORDON, G. H. (1910) *Ore deposits of New Mexico*, U. S. Geol. Survey Prof. Paper 68, p. 164-167

LINTON, ROBERT (1912) *Geology of Ocampo district*, Engr. Min. Jour., v. 94, p. 653-655

LOCKE, AUGUSTUS (1912) *Ore deposits of Goldfield*, Engr. Min. Jour., v. 94, p. 797-802, 843-849

LOPEZ NUÑEZ, MAURILIO (1928) *Angangueo, Miohoacan*, Boletín Minero, Oct.

McCOY, ALEX W. (1934) *An interpretation of local structural development in Mid-continent area associated with deposits of petroleum*, in *Problems of Petroleum Geology*, Am. Assoc. Petrol. Geol., p. 581-627

MAIN, FREDERICK H. (1956) *Geology and ore deposits, Indé-Cieneguillas district, Durango, Mexico*, 20th Int. Geol. Congr., Mexico, Abstracts, p. 286

MATSON, E. J. (1946) *Exploration of the Mt. Hope mine, Eureka Co., Nevada*, U. S. Bur. Mines Report Investig. 3928, 7 p.

McLAUGHLIN, R. P. (1907) *Geology of the Bodie district, California*, Min. Sci. Press, June 22, p. 795-796

MOEHLMAN, R. S. (1936) *Ore deposition south of Ouray, Colorado*, Econ. Geol., v. 31, p. 377-397, 488-504

NEVIN, C. M. (1949) *Principles of structural geology*, 4th ed., John Wiley & Sons, N. Y., p. 20

NEWHOUSE, W. H. (1931) *Some relations of ore deposits to folded rocks*, Am. Inst. Min. Met. Engrs. Trans., 1931 vol., p. 224-245

NOLAN, T. B. (1930) *Underground geology of western part of Tonopah mining district, Nevada*, Univ. Nev. Bull., v. 24, no. 4, p. 5-35

———— (1935) *Underground geology of Tonopah mining district, Nevada*, Univ. Nev. Bull., v. 29, no. 5, p. 1-49

———— (1936) *Tuscarora mining district*, Univ. Nev. Bull., v. 30, no. 1, 38 p.

PARKER, TRAVIS J., AND McDOWELL, A. N. (1951) *Scale models as guide to interpretation of salt-dome faulting*, Am. Assoc. Petrol. Geol. Bull., v. 35, p. 2076-2086

PARSONS, W. H. (1937) *The ore deposits of the Sunlight region, Park Co., Wyoming*, Econ. Geol., v. 32, p. 832-854

———— (1939) *Volcanic centers of the Sunlight area, Park Co., Wyoming*, Jour. Geol., v. 47, p. 1-26

PERRY, V. D. (1935) *Copper deposits of Cananea district, Sonora, Mexico*, 16th Int. Geol. Congr., *Copper resources of the world*, p. 413-418

PRESCOTT, BASIL (1926) *Underlying principles of the limestone replacement deposits of the Mexican province,* Engr. Min. Jour., v. 122, p. 246-253, 289-296

RANSOME, F. L. (1901a) *Ore deposits of the Rico Mountains, Colorado,* U. S. Geol. Survey 22nd Ann. Report, II, p. 229-397

———— (1901b) *Economic geology of the Silverton quadrangle, Colorado,* U. S. Geol. Survey Bull. 182, p. 87-92

———— (1909a) *Geology and ore deposits of Goldfield, Nevada,* U. S. Geol. Survey Prof. Paper 66, p. 155

———— (1909b) *Notes on some mining districts in Humboldt Co., Nevada,* U. S. Geol. Survey Bull. 414, p. 14-25

RANSOME, F. L., EMMONS, W. H., AND GARREY, G. H. (1910) *Geology and ore deposits of the Bullfrog district, Nevada,* U. S. Geol. Survey Bull. 407, 125 p.

RICHEY, J. E., THOMAS, H. H., *et al.* (1930) *Geology of Ardnamurchan, Northwest Mull and Coll,* Mem. Geol. Survey Scotland, p. 61-62, 93

RICKARD, T. A. (1924) *Ahumada lead mine and ore deposits of the Los La mentos Range, Mexico,* Engr. Min. Jour., v. 118, p. 365-373

ROBINSON, H. H. (1913) *San Francisco volcanic field, Arizona,* U. S. Geol. Survey Prof. Paper 76, p. 70-74

ROSS, C. P. (1941) *Quicksilver deposits of the Terlingua region, Texas,* Econ. Geol., v. 36, p. 115-142

SANTILLÁN, M. (1929) *Geología minera de la region comprendida entre Durango, Durango y Mazatlán, Sinaloa,* etc., Inst. Geol. de México, Bol. 48, p. 4-41

SCHMITT, HARRISON (1931) *Geology of the Parral area of the Parral district, Mexico,* Am. Inst. Min. Met. Engrs. Trans., General vol., p. 268-289

———— (1935) *Central mining district, New Mexico,* Am. Inst. Min. Met. Engrs. Trans., v. 115, p. 187-208

———— (1950a) *Origin of the "epithermal" deposits,* Econ. Geol., v. 45, p. 191-200

———— (1950b) *Genetic classification of the bed rock hypogene mineral deposits,* Econ. Geol., v. 45, p. 671-680

SCHRADER, F. C. (1923) *Jarbridge mining district, Nevada,* U. S. Geol. Survey Bull. 741, 86 p.

———— (1913) *Notes on the Antelope district, Nevada,* U. S. Geol. Survey Bull. 530, p. 87-98

———— (1935) *Contact mining district, Nevada,* U. S. Geol. Survey Bull. 847A, p. 1-41

SCHROTER, A. AUSTIN (1935) *A geologist visits the Mohave mining district,* Engr. Min. Jour., v. 136, p. 185-188

SCHUETTE, C. N. (1931) *Occurrence of quicksilver ore bodies,* Am. Inst. Min. Met. Engrs. Trans., 1931 vol., p. 403-488

SEARLS, FRED JR. (1948) *Contribution to the published information on geology and ore deposits of Goldfield, Nevada,* Univ. Nev. Bull., v. 42, p. 14, 19, 21

SELLARDS, E. H., BAKER, C. L., AND ROSS, C. P. (1934) *Geology of Texas,* v. II, p. 177-180, 529-548, 558-567

SINGEWALD, Q. D., AND BUTLER, B. S. (1931) *Preliminary report on the Russia mine, Park Co., Colorado,* Colo. Sci. Soc. Proc., v. 12, no. 12, p. 389-406

SPOONER, W. C. (1929) *Homer oil field, Claiborne Parish, Louisiana,* in *Structure of typical American oil fields,* Am. Assoc. Petrol. Geol., v. 1, p. 196-228

SPURR, J. E. (1905) *Geology of Tonopah mining district,* U. S. Geol. Survey Prof. Paper 42, 295 p.

———— (1916) *Relation of ore deposition to faulting,* Econ. Geol., v. 11, p. 608-610

———— (1923) *The ore magmas,* McGraw-Hill Book Co., N. Y., p. 339, 366-367, 696-697

SPURR, J. E., GARREY, G. H., AND FENNER, C. N. (1912) *Study of a contact metamorphic deposit,* Econ. Geol., v. 7, p. 444-484

STEWART, L. A. (1947) *Apache iron deposit, Navajo Co., Arizona,* U. S. Bur. Mines Report Investig. 4093, 87 p.

STONE, J., AND MCCARTHY, J. C. (1948) *Mineral and metal variations in the veins of Fresnillo, Zacatecas, Mexico,* Am. Inst. Min. Met. Engrs. Trans., v. 178, p. 91-106

STORMS, W. H. (1892) *San Bernardino Co., California,* in State Mineralogist's Report, no. 11, p. 347-349

TAYLOR, ALVIN V. JR. (1942) *Quartz Hill district, near Divide, Montana,* in *Ore deposits in relation to structural features,* Princeton Univ. Press, p. 215-216

TERRONES BENÍTEZ, ALBERTO (1922) *The camp of Guanecevi,* Engr. Min. Jour., v. 114, p. 139-144

THOM, W. T. JR. (1923) *The relation of deep-seated faults to the surface structural features of central Montana,* Am. Assoc. Petrol. Geol. Bull., v. 7, p. 1-13

THOM, W. T. JR. AND SPIEKER, EDMUND M. (1913) *Significance of geologic conditions in Naval Petroleum Reserve No. 3, Wyoming,* U. S. Geol. Survey Prof. Paper 113, 19 p.

UDDEN, J. A. (1907) *Sketch of the geology of the Chisos country, Brewster Co., Texas,* Univ. Texas Bull. 93, 101 p.

———— (1911) *Structural relations of quicksilver deposits,* Mining World, v. 34, p. 973-975

———— (1918) *The anticlinal theory as applied to some quicksilver deposits,* Univ. Texas Bull. 1822, 30 p.

UMPLEBY, J. B. (1913) *Geology and ore deposits of Lemhi Co., Idaho,* U. S. Geol. Survey Bull. 528, p. 127-134

VANDERWILT, J. W. (1932) *Preliminary geological notes on Galena Mt., a part of Snowmass Mt., Colorado,* Colo. Sci. Soc. Proc., v. 13, no. 1, p. 1-25

VILLAFAÑA, E. (1921) *El distrito minero de Pinos, Zacatecas,* Boletín Minero, v. 12-2, p. 186-194

WANDKE, ALFRED AND MARTÍNEZ, JUAN (1928) *The Guanajuato mining district, Mexico,* Econ. Geol., v. 23, p. 1-44

WEED, W. H. (1900) *Geology of the Little Belt Mountains, Montana,* U. S. Geol. Survey 20th Ann. Report III, p. 257-461

WEED, W. H., AND PIRSSON, V. (1896) *Geology of Castle Mountain mining district, Montana,* U. S. Geol. Survey Bull. 139, 164 p.

———— (1898) *Geology and mineral resources of the Judith Mountains of Montana,* U. S. Geol. Survey 18th Ann. Report, v. 3, p. 437-623

———— (1925) *Possibilities of the Calico mining district,* Engr. Min. Jour., v. 119, p. 757-763

WEEKS, F. B. (1926) *Mineralized breccias at Calico, California,* Engr. Min. Jour., v. 121, p. 484

———— (1929) *Calico mining district,* Min. Met., v. 10, p. 531-534

WESTGATE, L. G., AND KNOPF, ADOLPH (1932) *Geology and ore deposits of Pioche district, Nevada,* U. S. Geol. Survey Prof. Paper 171, Pl. 1, Pl. 2, sec. E-E′

WINCHELL, H. V. (1922) *Geology of Pachuca and El Oro, Mexico,* Am. Inst. Min. Engrs. Trans, v. 66, p. 36-40

WISSER, EDWARD (1937) *Formation of the north-south fractures of the Real del Monte area, Pachuca silver district, Mexico,* Am. Inst. Min. Met. Engrs. Trans., v. 126, p. 422-487

———— (1939) *Geologic parallels: Hog Mountain, Alabama and Paracale, Philippine Islands,* Econ. Geol., v. 34, p. 297-323

———— (1951) *Tectonic analysis of a mining district; Pachuca, Mexico,* Econ. Geol., v. 46, p. 459-477

INDEX

113